Date Due			
JL 10 '39			
Apr 28 '43			
Apr 28 '43			
May 18 '43			
May 20 '43			
May 26 '43			
Oct 17 '44			
July 15			
Dec 2 '54			
May 6 '66			
Apr 15 '67			
May 1 '67			

OUR ENEMY THE TERMITE

A portion of tests of timbers impregnated with chemical wood preservatives on Barro Colorado Island, Canal Zone, Panama, to determine the relative resistance of methods of impregnation and chemical preservatives in protecting wood from attack by termites. This site is a small cleared patch in a tropical jungle where many species of wood destroying termites occur.

OUR ENEMY THE
TERMITE

BY

THOMAS ELLIOTT SNYDER

Senior Entomologist of the Bureau of Entomology and Plant Quarantine of the United States Department of Agriculture

ITHACA · NEW YORK

COMSTOCK PUBLISHING COMPANY, INC.

1935

PRINTED IN THE UNITED STATES OF AMERICA
THE PLIMPTON PRESS, NORWOOD, MASS.

To

My Wife

PREFACE

HAVING spent twenty-six years in piecing out the life history of our native termites or " white ants " from actual observations in the field and information gained by studying the habits of these insects in artificial colonies in the laboratory, I was greatly intrigued recently by an " Alice in Wonderland " account of termites in a popular magazine. Two big game hunters had their interest aroused by reading Maeterlinck's fascinating book entitled *Life of the Termites*. The life of darkness of these creatures, the underground tyranny, the cruelty, the sordid avarice — a life revolting though crowned by sacrifices — Maeterlinck has described in a masterly manner. Who would penetrate these living tombs? The brave adventurers, with the aid of modern science, were able to lift the veil obscuring the hidden life of the termites. Voluntarily exposing themselves to certain rays under a bell jar, the men succeeded in reducing themselves to a size so small as to enable them to penetrate and explore the galleries in the nest of a colony of tropical termites. Their relatively diminutive size rendered this a real peril, since they were at the mercy not only of the termites, but also of ants, enemies of termites seeking to raid the termites. This hazardous enterprise, after many perilous adventures rivaling big game hunting, was finally successful, and they even penetrated into that holy of holies, the domed " royal cell " where the king and queen are kept in state.

The following account of the habits of the termites native to the United States could be made much more complete if some such bizarre method of exploring the labyrinth of galleries and the recesses of termite nests could be undertaken. Even then, careful and tedious observations over periods of years would be necessary to learn anything of their manner of living.

Since 1909 the author has been associated with the Bureau of Entomology of the United States Department of Agriculture.

His principal assignment during this period has had to do with studies of termites and other insects which injure wooden products and with experiments to develop more effective methods for their control. This book is based very largely on the experience gained during this period and on the activities carried on in connection with official work. The author makes acknowledgment that in the preparation of the book he has freely consulted information assembled in his work with the United States Bureau of Entomology. This is particularly true with regard to the section dealing with artificial methods for the suppression of termites, where the control suggested is essentially that recommended by the Bureau of Entomology in its various publications. The author, however, assumes full responsibility for the selection, the arrangement, and the method of presentation of the material included in this treatise. He wishes to thank the Chief of the Bureau of Entomology for authorizing the use of illustrations and data from the extensive files of that Bureau. Most of the illustrations are reprinted from papers by the author published either in technical journals or in bulletins of the United States Department of Agriculture or in the Proceedings of the United States National Museum.

A glossary of technical terms will be found at the end of the volume.

THOMAS ELLIOTT SNYDER

Washington, D. C.
June, 1935

CONTENTS

CONTENTS

xii CONTENTS

OUR ENEMY THE TERMITE

CHAPTER I

TERMITES: WHAT THEY ARE

IMAGINE a human society, established by eugenic selection, which breeds and raises men in test tubes where individuals are " conditioned " by methods of psychological suggestion to play their rôle. Men would not be born free and equal in this Utopian state; there would be formed social classes and well defined rights and a division of labor as in the caste system in India. Such is the interesting social system of termites or " white ants ".

In his satire on a conjectural future human society, *Oh, Brave New World,* Aldous Huxley has unwittingly given a very accurate picture of life in a termite colony. For, unlike the majority of insects, which live independent lives as individuals, termites live permanently together, in more or less fixed, organized communities. Insects which live a social life in such large or small colonies are called " social insects " and include the ants, bees, and wasps, as well as the termites.

The members of these colonies are not all alike but are of different shapes and sizes, each especially adapted for certain duties in building, repairing, and caring for the nest, stocking it with food or replenishing it with young. There is a more or less closely-adhered-to division of labor.

Though sterile and lowly hewers of wood and drawers of water, the workers probably enact the most important rôle in the colony. However, they cannot reproduce their kind and so pass on characters to their progeny. Indeed their most important influence is exerted on their fellow colony members, but just how great is this coercion and how it is carried out is in considerable doubt.

The soldiers constitute the other sterile caste. These neuters were probably the forms from which the workers later developed. Soldiers are the warriors who protect the colony from insect raiders from the outside. They also act as a colony police force as well as a standing army for defense.

The building of the nest, its care, the search for food, are all
directed to the main object of insect societies, namely to produce many young for the maintenance of the species. Hence
sex is all-important and there are special forms which do nothing
but breed and produce young. Although the egg-laying females
or " queens " of the termites are enormously developed and have
a specialized, almost unique " post-adult " growth, the colony is
by no means a feminist society as are colonies of ants and bees.
There are "equal rights " for the male. The males continue
to live with and to fertilize the females or queens and these
" kings " also have a slight post-adult growth. (The " drone "
honey bee dies soon after he has mated with the female.) The
king and queen are the fertile forms that found and head the
colony and produce the young.

In no case today do termites exist which do not produce as
their progeny other castes, both fertile and sterile, in addition
to the winged sexual adult forms which establish new colonies.
It is believed that these winged forms are the ancestral type
which, before termites became social insects, existed as individual males and females, and that these sexual creatures associated together only to breed and raise young, which, in turn,
developed only to winged sexual forms.

The worker caste has been found as fossils only in the recent
Oligocene strata, whereas the winged, sexual adults (and probably also the sterile soldiers or defense caste) date back to the
older Eocene formations, or earliest division of the Tertiary
period. There is good evidence for the theory that the workers
were a later development or off-shoot from the soldier caste.
Soldiers are found in colonies of primitive termites which lack
workers. Traces of wings occur on the soldiers, especially on
soldiers of primitive termites, which shows that they sprang
directly from the sexual forms; workers have no trace of wings.

The number of different kinds or castes varies with the different groups of termites. In some groups there are no workers, in others no soldiers; and there is a great variation in the
type or form of the soldiers — as many as three different forms
may occur in the same nest. There is also variation among
different groups of termites in the kinds of sexual adults or reproductive forms.

The character of the progeny and the ratio between the numbers of the castes present in colonies also vary with the group and the age of the particular colony. Hence a genetic or hereditary formula for termites would vary similarly and no general formula would suffice for all groups of termites.

This brings us to the problem of how these different kinds or castes in the same species of termites were evolved. " Polymorphism " or the presence of different castes, some of them sterile, has ever been a troublesome stumbling block to the exponents of the various theories of evolution. How was the evolution of the castes of the social insects, such as the ants, bees, and termites, brought about? Charles Darwin frankly admitted in his *Origin of Species* that the question of how the characters of the sterile workers and soldiers — which do not reproduce — secure representation in the germ cells of the species cannot be satisfactorily explained by the theory which he advanced!

Thus there is no doubt that the study of termites and the solving of the mode of origin of the different castes would have a most important bearing on the whole general problem of evolution or development of life.

It can easily be seen that, quite aside from the damage they do, termites, with their social habits approaching the manner of living of men, afford interest not only to scientists but to the general public as well. As to the manner in which the production of the different forms or castes in the termite colonies of today is determined, there have been two views, both based on observation and experiment.

The first theory is that the young are all alike when they first hatch from the egg, but differentiate into the various adult castes through the influence of external factors of their immediate environment, such as food, the care they receive from the workers, etc.

The adherents to the second theory claim that the young are not all alike at the time of hatching, but that the castes are hereditary. Some if not all of the different castes are distinguishable from the beginning, and the castes are therefore predetermined in the egg or embryo by internal factors.

It is the opinion of the present writer that the origin of the termite castes is due to internal causes; that they are hereditary and of germinal origin. I can not believe that external stimuli can be credited with formative — indeed almost creative — powers. Which of these views is correct? Or are they both in part true? Only more careful studies will answer this question of such great interest to biologists.

A natural explanation is that the castes have originated by segregation from an unstable, hybrid form, whose progeny are not all similar to the parent which produced them. There do not seem to be any visible differences in the chromosomes in the germ cells of the various castes.

Dr. G. B. Castle of the University of California, as a result of experimental work, has recently advanced a food inhibition theory. Namely, in colonies where reproductive forms are fully functioning the development of any additional young sexual adults is inhibited by the secretions of the parent reproductives (king and queen). These secretions are transmitted to the young by the grooming habit in which the young lick exudation off the bodies of the adults.

This theory appears to be most plausible and great interest will be attached to further studies with other kinds of termites. Castle's experiments were made only with colonies of the " rotten wood " termites of the Pacific Coast, a primitive, plastic type.

" Communism " in the human sense means common ownership of property and state control, supposedly for the benefit of the working class. Among the social insects, as in the termites, there is a state bordering on communism. The rights of the individual, his actions, work, property, and food, are subordinated to the demands of colony life. The survival of the colony and the species, not the individual and the species, is the dominant rule of the association. Individuals or even castes may perish so that the community may survive. No sentimentalism occurs in this efficient organization.

What is the controlling element in the colony? We can only answer — inherited instinct, or response to either internal or external stimuli, " tropic " behavior or reaction tendencies. The " spirit of the colony " or ruling master mind is not an individual or even a caste, but the collective instincts of a group of individuals and castes. If we attempt to go farther among insects we incur the danger of becoming " anthropocentric ", endowing insects with manlike faculties, or even crediting insects with reasoning power. We can not say that insects react as does man.   They see differently and their senses of touch, taste, and smell function quite differently.   Man can not measure all creation by his own yardstick!

Man and his civilization are comparatively young.   There have been ebbs and flows in man's development, but there has been consistent, if not continued, progress.   Termites, on the other hand, after having reached certain states of body and community development, have made no further progress.   Of course termites, as well as other insects, can not reason and are merely guided by hereditary instincts and impulses — hunger, sex, and fear being the primary stimuli.

The progress of termites was by evolutionary development, as was man's.   But man, with reasoning powers and individual initiative, has been able in his comparatively short history (geologically speaking) to surpass all other forms of animal life.

We can see that " our enemy the termite " is an interesting creature who has alternately puzzled and fascinated men.   I shall now attempt to describe in detail the origin of termites, discuss their closest relatives, and explain how termites live. Finally, we must learn how and why they damage man's property, and how such damage can be prevented and remedied.

Termites are among the world's longest lived insects, and certain forms take years to develop and mature: termite queens in artificial colonies are known to have lived for twenty-five years.   Since most termites are blind and soft-bodied, need much humidity and shun the light, they always conceal themselves within wood, in the earth, or within their earth-like shelter tubes; thus they are protected from their enemies and from lack of moisture and consequent drying up.   Hence, their secluded and confined or claustral habits render termites very difficult to study, much more so than the dominant ants, which often run about in the open.

Known and investigated for hundreds of years because of their destructiveness to buildings constructed by man, the contents of these buildings, man's crops and other property, there are still many wide gaps in our knowledge of termite economy. The biology of termites is far from simple; and their socialistic habits, aside from their destructiveness, make a fascinating study.

For, as we have shown, unlike the majority of insects, which live as individuals, termites live permanently together in more or less fixed, organized communities. Insects which live in such large or small colonies with different forms or castes and a division of labor are called " social insects "; included are the ants, bees, and wasps, which, however, lead quite different lives from the termites.

Wingless, sterile workers and soldiers of both sexes are included in the parent colony in addition to the winged or wingless sexual adults and young; that is, there is a " caste system ", and not only do termites live communally, but also each colony consists of different forms of the same species or kind. There may be two or more different types of the same caste in the same species, and often as many as seven different kinds occur in the same nest. Each caste has more or less precisely demarked duties to perform. Hence, there is a division of labor in the termite community; every effort put forth by the individual must be for the common welfare, if the colony is to survive.

CLASSIFICATION

While grouped in the popular mind with the other social insects, termites are systematically classified in a lower and more primitive order — the Isoptera or similar-winged insects. There are also marked differences in the life habits of termites from those of the other social insects, which are all in the order Hymenoptera or membrane-winged insects — a highly specialized group. The Hymenoptera are younger geologically as well as less primitive than the termites. Social life is confined to these two orders and there has been a remarkable parallel development of castes and of polymorphism. The more lowly termites seem to have been more plastic than the ants, bees, and wasps, and have gone further in developing different forms within the species. The castes among termites are also more definitely defined and more stable than among the ants and bees.

It is unfortunate that there is such world-wide common usage of the name " white ants " for termites, which are not ants, nor are they white. It is true that the workers of some termites, including our common subterranean species, are of a dirty-white color; but in other termites workers are much more dark colored. Most of the young, however, are usually whitish and of course are superficially ant-like. All of the winged adults are colored, ranging from pale yellow to black. Some of the other vernacular names for termites are " wood lice ", " come-jen ", " cupim ", " carcoma ", and " polilla " in the Americas; " weisse Ameisen " and " fourmis blanches " in Europe, and " anay " in the Philippines. Of course, some of these names are merely translations of the words, white ants.

While termites, as has been shown, are not true ants, in form of body they are superficially ant-like and they live a similar life in large colonies or nests made up of different castes, even more varied than among the ants. Termites have a thicker thorax or " waist " than ants, which have very slim waists. In ants the fore wings are markedly larger than the hind wings, whereas in termites the wings are nearly of the same size. However, later we shall show that the termites are closely related to the roaches, to which we can see but little resemblance without close study.

In the entire world there are five major groups or families in the order Isoptera. Included in this order are 152 genera or subgenera (minor groups), and 1978 described species or kinds, including varieties and subspecies. This enumeration includes fossils as well as living termites. From Table I (see Addenda), it might be noted that among living termites the greater number are among the higher or more specialized forms, while the fossil termites are represented by a relatively greater number of primitive or generalized forms. It is believed that the species of termites as yet undiscovered will raise the total number to approximately five thousand kinds.

DISTRIBUTION

LIVING TERMITES. Termites are widely distributed throughout the world and living species occur in all of the zoögeographical regions except the Arctic and Antarctic. A study of termites preserved as fossils in stone, amber, and gum copal will reveal that in prehistoric times there was an even wider distribution of these insects throughout the world.

At present, the African or Ethiopian region is richest in number of species; the Neotropical or tropical American termite fauna includes the next greatest number of species; then come the Oriental and Australian zoögeographical regions with large numbers of termite species; and finally the North American or Nearctic and Palaearctic termite fauna, with relatively few species.

But compared to the enormous numbers of individuals of the different castes in the nests, there are but relatively few

genera (groups) and species (kinds). America north of Mexico has but 56 species, representing but 3 families and 14 genera or subgenera (Table II: see Addenda). Termites probably occur in every state in the Union, but so far we do not have actual record of any species occurring in North Dakota.

On the American Continent, certain species have been found as far north as the Quesnal Lake region in British Columbia, latitude 52° and 30′. Termites have also been recorded from Ontario, Canada. Furthermore, these insects occur at high altitudes in the Rocky Mountains and Pacific Coast Range, reaching elevations

Fig. 1. Dead southern cypress tree on slope of sand dunes at Cape Henry, Va., infested with the dry-wood termite, *Kalotermes approximatus* Sny.

of 7000–8000 feet. To the south, Patagonia seems to be the limit of their distribution, at about the same latitude as their northern limit.

Thus, we see that termites are by no means confined to the tropical regions of the world, but occur in the temperate regions even as far north as Mediterranean Europe and North America.

On the Pacific Coast of North America, the rotten wood termites, the species of *Zoötermopsis*, occur farther north in British Columbia than do subterranean termites, the species of *Reticulitermes*. The dry-wood termites, species of *Kalo-*

termes, do not occur as far north as British Columbia, but occur in northern California and Washington. This is a much more northern distribution than *Kalotermes* has on the Atlantic Coast. At Fort Ross in Sonoma County, California, *K. minor* Hag. was found in 1927 in a building in cured redwood 104 years old.

On the Atlantic Coast, a species of *Kalotermes* occurs as far north as Cape Henry, Virginia, where it is found in only a few dead cypress trees, all on the steep back slope of the highest dunes, where the slope is at an angle of nearly 45° (fig. 1). Colonies evidently pass the winter in the interior of the wood when they leave the outer layers of the wood of these trees.

It is exceedingly interesting to find this termite *K. approximatus* Snyder at Cape Henry, Virginia, in the desert region which, with its forest of cypress, tupelo gum, magnolia, holly, etc., and the tangle of vines, including yellow jessamine, is characteristic of the flora of Florida. Many tree branches are covered with resurrection fern, and mistletoe is common on the gum trees. There is Spanish moss on some of the live oak trees.

Before the discovery of this termite in 1923 at Cape Henry, the farthest north that any eastern species of *Kalotermes* had been found was at Charleston, South Carolina. This was in the spring of 1922 when I was returning from my wedding trip in the south. Half an hour before train time I saw termite pellets in a telegraph pole, and since at this time Savannah, Georgia, was the known northern limit of *Kalotermes* I was greatly excited. Directing my wife to go on to the hotel and get the baggage to the depot, I dashed into a hardware store, purchased a hatchet and chopped into the pole on one of Charleston's main business streets. I got my specimen, a soldier. Why I was not arrested and how I caught the train are questions which I have never satisfactorily answered to a very perturbed new wife.

None of the termites inhabiting the United States can definitely be said to have been introduced, although some species overlap in distribution into Canada, the West Indies, and Central and South America. It is to be expected that insects will adhere to the limitations of life zones and natural laws but not to political boundaries and man-made laws.

Of course in the United States the greatest number of species

and also of individuals occurs in the warmer, more southern
sections. Arizona has the largest number with 25 species, representing 9 genera or subgenera. In Texas are found 20 species
in 8 genera. California has 19 species included in 7 genera.
In Florida have been found 15 species in 6 genera. Nevada
has 8 species in 5 genera. The other states range from 1 to 5
species each.

States also are political divisions and mean nothing in nature.
In general, however, the above tabulation shows that the more
southern regions have the richest fauna.

But little collecting has been done in some sparsely settled
states, and future changes are to be expected in state lists of
termites. New species should be discovered especially in Texas,
New Mexico, Arizona, and Florida. I hope some day again to
explore wild areas in various localities in the United States
searching for new species or studying the habits of obscure
species. For while in the tropics there are many localities that
present wonderful opportunities for the study of termites, our
native species are also well worth studying and in this country
we have just as interesting and magnificent scenery about their
habitats.

I have investigated termites midst the striking virgin wild
growth of the southern Appalachian Mountains; in the sub-
tropical everglades of Florida; on ocean islands or offshore
keys in Florida; on the plains, prairies, and deserts of the west;
in canyons in the southwest rimmed by pink and purple cliffs;
on the slopes of the Rocky Mountains and Sierras; and among
the majestic big trees of the Pacific Coast. Especially when one
is camping alone, the primeval beauties of mountain, forest,
and desert scenery profoundly impress the imagination.

There is great need for further ecological studies of the
termites in relation to their environment. While species of
nasutiform termites (*Nasutitermes*), or termites with a nose-
like projection on the front of the head, where there is a gland
secreting a fluid used in defense, occur in the West Indies or
Antilles and Middle America, as well as in Texas and Arizona
(as species of the subgenus *Tenuirostritermes*), strangely
enough no *Nasutitermes* occur either in Florida or California.
Certain localities appear to be favorable, while in others apparently as suitable termites do not occur. As an illustration,

termites after doing damage to a building sometimes will abandon the wood for apparently no reason. The cause may be disease, raiding ants, unfavorable climatic environment, or some cause not apparent to man.

Also, in the tropics where termites are as a rule wide-spread and occur in enormous numbers there will be certain local regions where but few occur. These areas appear as isolated spots or islands on a faunal map, or map of the termite life of the region. Why are they not inhabited by termites? If we could find out, doubtless clues important in the control of termites might be uncovered.

FOSSIL TERMITES. Fossil termites or prehistoric termites embedded in rock, amber, or gum copal have been found in

FIG. 2.   Wing of a fossil termite, *Stylotermes washingtonensis* Sny., found in Miocene rock in the State of Washington. Enlarged 5 times.

various parts of the world and are well represented in the fauna or among the animal life of the Old World, often in localities where no living termites occur or where far different species occur today. The ages of these fossils prove that termites antedated not only man but also the worst and most consistent enemies of termites — the ants.

Some of the remains of insects at first identified as fossil termites have been proven to be other insects, and also fossil insects classified in other orders have recently been proven to be termites. As a result, there lately has been considerable revision; and the status of fossil termites and the former climate and fauna and flora that they imply have undergone rather drastic changes. A more conservative and moderate view is now taken of the changes which have taken place in the prehistoric topography and climate of the localities where the fossil termites have been discovered.

In the United States, nine fossil termites have been found in the states of Washington, Colorado, and Tennessee. A fossil wing of *Stylotermes washingtonensis* Sny. found in the Miocene rock of Washington may be fifty-five million years old (fig. 2); *Stylotermes* is now only represented by one living species in Southern India. Recent discoveries in the field of radium activity enable man to date back the age of the world much farther: it is far older than thought by the earlier, too conservative palaeontologists, and consequently fossils are older.

Fɪɢ. 3. Hind wing of *Mastotermes darwiniensis* Froggatt of Australia; note the resemblance to the wing of the cockroach (Blattidae). Greatly enlarged.

In western Tennessee, in the lower Eocene, occurs a fossil species of the world's most primitive and roach-like termite genus *Mastotermes,* a genus now only known by a single living species in northern Australia (fig. 3). Fossils in this genus also occur in England, where today there are no living termites.

At Florissant, Colorado, in the Miocene shale rocks, which are at least several million years old, have been found fossil termites in two genera which are now represented by living species in the United States; namely *Termopsis* and *Reticulitermes.* Here at present, probably because of the high altitude, no living termites have been found, although a species of *Reticulitermes* occurs at near-by localities. Species of the subterranean *Reticulitermes* do not occur on the mountains of western United States at elevations higher than between 7,000 and 8,000 feet.

In the same strata of Miocene rock at Florissant where occur these fossil termites are embedded small twigs of a redwood or Sequoia tree; today this group of trees is represented by only two living species, which grow in California and Oregon on the Pacific Coast. These majestic redwoods are our oldest and tallest North American evergreen or coniferous trees. Large fossil stumps of Sequoia trees also occur at Florissant.

At present only three species of living *Zoötermopsis* or " rotten wood " termites occur; two in the Pacific Coast region, overlapping with the distribution of the Sequoia, and one in Arizona

Fig. 4. Winged adult of *Reticulitermes minimus* Snyder in Baltic Sea amber. Enlarged.

and New Mexico. *Termopsis* may be the fossil prototype of *Zoötermopsis.*

Another fossil species of *Reticulitermes* has recently been found in the Miocene shale rocks at Creede, Colorado. No living termites occur at Creede.

Species of *Reticulitermes* are to be found living throughout temperate North America and indeed in the north temperate zone throughout the world. As fossils, species of *Reticulitermes* are found not only in shale rock but also in Europe in amber washed ashore from the bottom of the Baltic Sea (fig. 4). Amber is the fossilized resin from a coniferous tree of the Lower Oligocene period, many millions of years old.

At Florissant in 1917 the writer, after a day's vain digging for fossil termites, purchased from Mr. G. W. Wilson (in charge of the fossil pits) a large winged termite embedded in Miocene shale. In this identical specimen of shale, at a corresponding depth and on the same surface, are impressions of small twigs of Sequoia. The termite is now extinct and is the primitive *Prokalotermes hageni* Scudder (fig. 5).

One might imagine the Florissant Basin several million years ago, in the twilight of a warm summer evening in June or July, possibly after a heavy rain. Fairly large numbers of large,

Fig. 5. Winged primitive fossil termite (*Prokalotermes hageni* Scud.)
from Miocene shale at Florissant,
Colo. Enlarged 2 times. *Photo. by
Dr. R. S. Bassler.*

strong-flying, colonizing termites flit about near the shores of the lake, seeking in dead coniferous trees, logs, or stumps, crevices in which the males and females can establish new colonies. Many of these adventurous winged adults are carried out over the lake by the wind and their romance is ended by falling into the water.

Although they thus perish, their life was not in vain, for today they have been exhumed from their tombs in the Tertiary shale rocks; and, together with the fossil plants and other animals, they enable scientists to unfold the drama of the period in which they lived. The story is incomplete, indeed far from a Pepys' diary, but there is sufficient to show the general topography and the mountain fauna and flora of the region.

In Florida, fossil pellets of partly digested, excreted wood of a dry-wood termite (*Kalotermes* sp.) have been found in the Seminole Pleistocene formation. This is a fairly recent period and relics are sub-fossil in character. Man was present in the Pleistocene period.

Most termite fossils are of winged adults or wings of extinct species that were entombed in resin during the swarm, or fell into the shallow water or mud of the prehistoric lake beds. Fossils of termites in the highly specialized family Termitidae have not been found in more ancient Baltic amber, but occur in rocks and gum copal. This gum is an exudation from a tropical tree (*Trachylobium mossambicense* Klotsch) which is still extant and occurs in Africa.

Gum copal is not as old geologically as Baltic amber; it is found in the more recent Pleistocene formation or during the Age of Man. The higher or more specialized termites are well-represented in gum copal, not only as winged adults but also as soldiers of both mandibulate and nasutiform types. Some species are very well preserved and are identical with termites found living today in Africa.

Thus, by means of fragmentary bits of rock, resin, or gum containing often only parts of insects, animals, and plants, and the fauna and flora that they imply, it is possible to reconstruct the world as it existed millions of years ago in prehistoric times. Even the climate is indicated by the type of life present.

HISTORY OF THE ORIGIN AND DEVELOPMENT OF TERMITES

The ancestors of our present insect fauna must have had a long descent, and fossils doubtless appeared earlier than the last part of the Carboniferous or coal measures. This was during the Age of the Amphibians and Lycopods or large fernlike trees. The ancestors of such fossils were the large roaches or Blattidae, and they are therefore among the oldest insects. Indeed the Pennsylvanian period might be termed the Age of Roaches. These prehistoric insects were not, however, the immediate ancestors of our living species.

Termites, while they have a close systematic relationship with the roaches, are much younger or more recently evolved. No termites are known from the Mesozoic Age, the Age of the giant Reptiles; but they may have then existed. Termites have been found as fossils in all deposits from the Lower Tertiary on; that is, from the end of the Age of Reptiles to the beginning of the Age of Mammals. While archaic, they are not nearly as ancient as the roaches. In a certain prehistoric period roaches were among the dominant forms of insect life, and were of relatively huge size. Roaches were so common that this early period

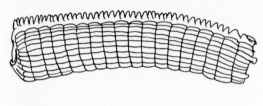

Fig. 6. Egg mass of the primitive roach (*Cryptocercus punctulatus* Scud.). The number of eggs or embryos in an egg mass or ootheca aimed at by nature is apparently 32, or one from each ovariole, although the number varies considerably. The eggs are arranged in a double row. Each egg is enclosed in a membrane and the double-rowed packet is enclosed by a thick, cellophane-like membrane, with nine ridges on each side, a smooth ventral surface, and a laced-up or " zippered " dorsal surface. Enlarged 7½ times. *After Cleveland*.

has been termed the " Age of Roaches ". Termites were never so dominant in prehistoric times.

Probably both termites and roaches are offshoots of a more primitive common ancestor or prototype of earlier development than either termites or roaches. Insect fossils are constantly being discovered and with them certain forms that might be termed " connecting links " between related orders of insects.

None of the fossil termites are more primitive than forms living today. The most primitive living species (*Mastotermes darwiniensis* Frogg.) has wing structure similar to roaches, as

well as an egg mass similar to the egg capsule of roaches (fig. 6) ,
indicating at least a common ancestry. The individual termite
eggs are firmly cemented together by a light brown gelatinous
secretion which fills the interstices between the eggs (fig. 7) .
In the wings of certain primitive roaches, a break occurs similar
to the humeral suture or line of weakness near the base of the
termite wing, where the wings break off after the colonizing
flight. There are other similarities based both on biology and
on homologous structures, but termites have become more
highly specialized and have become social in habit and have
evolved a caste system.

Roaches of even the most primitive type are at most only
sub-social or aggregate in habit; the family group remains to-

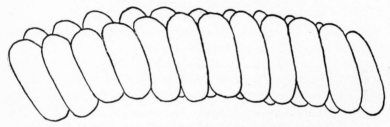

Fig. 7. Egg mass of the primitive roach-like termite *Mastotermes darwiniensis*
Frogg. 22 to 24 eggs are in the mass. Length of mass about $\frac{1}{5}$ inch. Enlarged 20 times. *After Hill.*

gether while the young are being reared. They are seldom
found boring in sound wood, with the exception of a large,
primitive, wingless brown roach (*Cryptocercus punctulatus*
Scudder). This roach leads a sub-social life, burrowing in the
fairly sound wood in partly decayed logs, where the wood serves
as both shelter and food. Its distribution is discontinuous,
since it occurs in the Southern Appalachian Mountains, in
Maryland near Washington, D. C., and on the Pacific Coast.

Studies by Dr. L. R. Cleveland, now of Harvard University,
have shown that the intestinal protozoa of this roach are very
similar to those found in a symbiotic, or mutual benefit, relationship in the intestines of termites. Here, due to the action of enzymes, wood particles ingested by the protozoa are
broken down and made available as food for the host termites.

In most roaches, protozoa do not occur as free living forms, but are encysted, or lie curled up, enclosed in a sac. Possibly termites originally obtained their protozoa from such wood-boring roaches. In California, this roach (*Cryptocercus*) and species of *Zoötermopsis* — the rotten wood termites — have been found inhabiting the same log. The pellets of excreta of this roach are longer, but much more slender than those of *Zoötermopsis*. *Cryptocercus* is slower moving than most roaches, but as rapid as the primitive Australian *Mastotermes*, which moves more rapidly than most termites.

While termites, as can be observed from both living and fossil species, have progressed from primitive, generalized forms to the more highly specialized species, such as the fungus culti-vators of Africa, India and Malaya, they have made no further recent progress. They probably had reached their complete structural and social development, including the caste system, in the early Tertiary. Since these prehistoric periods, they have undergone very little modification.

During phylogeny or evolutionary development, termites have lost more or at least as much as they have gained. This applies not only to structure (observed in the loss in body size, the soldiers' jaws or mandibles, and strength of flight), but also to the social system or castes (loss of the soldier and apterous or wingless reproductive form). Furthermore, losses can be noted in those functions stimulated by the primary urges of hunger (loss of symbiotic protozoa) and sex and fear (underground or secluded life).

Of course, progressive development can also be seen, where there is greater specialization in food (fungi and lichens), re-production (greater rate of egg laying), and defense (wonder-ful architecture, rain-shedding and well ventilated nests). In general, however, termites have not made continued, consistent progress since prehistoric times, when they had practically reached the peak of their evolution.

The more archaic termites have been suppressed by the more dominant and much more numerous ants. While ants, the worst enemies of termites, over-run certain regions of the world, termites have been forced to under-run or undermine them. It is noteworthy that the most effective foes of termites are not insects that live as individuals, but another group of social insects.

Certain termites, particularly those with nasutiform soldiers, can repel ants raiding their colonies for food. By means of the glandular secretion, they drive away the marauders. Other species, such as soldiers of " powder-post " termites, species of *Cryptotermes,* block up galleries in the wood with their peculiarly modified heads (fig. 8). Other ants, raiding mound nests of termites for both food and a home, can be walled off by termites rapidly repairing breaches in their nests. Some tropical ants, indeed, will not attack or eat termites.

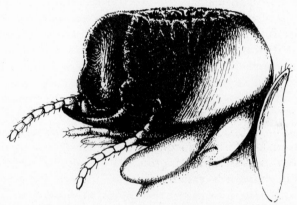

FIG. 8.   Head of soldier of a " powder-post " termite
(*Cryptotermes brevis* Walk.) adapted for blocking up
tunnels in wood to exclude enemies.   Greatly enlarged.

In addition to the roaches, other close insect relatives of termites today are the gregarious, web-spinning embiids, earwigs, zorapterids, and the peculiar archaic " cricket-roaches " or grylloblattids found in the snow fields of western North America. None of these insects are really social in habit, but some lead sub-social lives, where there is a beginning of colony life.

In only one group, namely the zorapterids, is there evidence of a possible beginning or trace of a caste system. These small, active insects, living a gregarious life, in habitats similar to those of termites, have both winged and wingless reproductive types; the winged sexual forms shed their wings as do colonizing termites.

The zorapterids (or " wingless forms of life ") had been described from wingless forms, and the writer over eleven years ago found the first winged adults in an artificial colony in captivity which he had collected in southern Florida. Hence, the name of these odd creatures, which somewhat resemble book-lice, is now not appropriate. There is still considerable discussion as to their true position in classification. I believe they are very closely related to the termites, with whom they 'were first found. At first they were believed to be guests in termite colonies, but later it was proven that they merely inhabit similar environments.

The roaches, which are among the oldest of insects, have survived from the Carboniferous rocks to the present time with but little structural modification. They appear extremely well adapted to changing environment. However, they probably will never markedly change, but always will maintain the same general habitus or form. In the struggle for existence, development or evolution occurs by natural selection of variations. The fittest or most adaptable will survive; those too specialized will perish.

Collections of termites from all over the world sent to the United States National Museum to be identified are always eagerly and hopefully examined by the writer for new forms, especially when from remote corners of the world such as Borneo, Fiji, the Solomon Islands, New Guinea, etc. Odd new genera and peculiar new species do turn up; I have also collected them alive in the tropics. In general, however, I am disappointed by seeing well-known genera appear under the microscope. Even the novelties, no matter how striking, possess the same general form. Each region, nevertheless, has produced one or more forms which are unique, at least in so far as living termites are concerned.

Unpromising or messy collections do sometimes yield unexpected novelties or rarities. As will be shown later, the gooey mass from a tropical anteater's stomach may yield a new genus of termites, rare ants and their guests, or the parasites of termite guests. Fragments of termites from the stomachs of toads or birds yield new forms or give interesting data on geographical distribution. It is sometimes very difficult to identify the fragments but it is worth while to solve the puzzle. Often a bottle of common termites when carefully examined will yield a rare guest of termites, a new fungus disease of termites or an abnormality or "intercaste", that is, a form intermediate between two normal castes.

Of course it is more fun to collect and study the living termites, but this takes much time and money; and collections sent in by volunteer collectors often yield valuable results, even though much time is wasted examining and classifying the usual common species.

CHAPTER II

METAMORPHOSIS AND DESCRIPTION
OF THE TERMITE CASTES

AMONG termites metamorphosis is said to be incomplete, for there is no pupa or inactive (over a long period) non-feeding stage. There are three stages in the life of termites: the egg; the immature forms, the young (nymph); and the mature individual (including sterile workers, soldiers, and the various fertile winged or wingless reproductive forms) (fig. 9).

THE EGGS. The eggs are yellowish-white and kidney-shaped. There are differences in the sizes of the eggs: our largest and most primitive termites have the largest eggs (fig. 10).

THE NYMPHS OR YOUNG. All of the nymphs or young hatch from the eggs in the same general shape as the parents and are active at practically all times (fig. 11). There is neither a grub stage nor a long resting or pupal stage. The young all appear to be alike upon hatching; after a few molts, they can be separated into the small-headed reproductive types and the large-headed sterile forms (fig. 12). Most of the former attain short wing pads or buds, which gradually grow longer.

Instead of a long resting stage, the young are active except for relatively short " quiescent stages " (fig. 13). During these quiescent stages and following molts or shedding of the skin, marked changes and growth become apparent; but in general the most important changes both external and internal appear at the final molt. In this type of gradual development the termites again resemble the roaches.

The large-headed forms develop into mature sabre-jawed soldiers and sawtooth-jawed workers in species of our native *Reticulitermes*. The soldier develops from a worker-like form to the soldier. The worker caste may be merely an arrested stage of the soldier. Workers and soldiers develop to maturity in one year.

THE WORKERS. The soft-bodied, wingless, sterile " workers ",

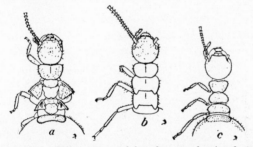

FIG. 9. *Above:* Three types of female reproductive forms or "queens" of the common subterranean termite of eastern U. S.; each type has a male of corresponding form: 1. queen developed from the winged adult, or macropterous type; 2. the short wing pad or brachypterous form; 3. the wingless or apterous form. When the normal, monogamous form (1) dies many of either of the other types, which are polygamous, take her place. It is useless to attempt to destroy a termite colony by hunting for and killing the queen — the brood or young must also be destroyed.
Below: Details of head and thorax.

with their saw-toothed jaws (fig. 14A) are in reality the destructive form and occur in the greatest numbers in colonies; these neuter forms are potentially both males and females. These workers make the excavations occupied by the colony and en-

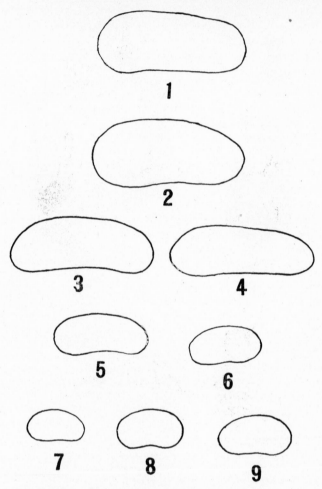

FIG. 10. Eggs of native termites in nine groups or genera.
　 1. Primitive Pacific Coast rotten wood termite (*Zoötermopsis angusti-*
　 collis Hag.)
　 2. Southern moist wood termite (*Neotermes castaneus* Burm.)
　 3. Southern dry-wood termite (*Kalotermes schwarzi* Bks.)
　 4. Southern powder-post termite (*Cryptotermes cavifrons* Bks.)
　 5. The Florida Prorhinotermes (*Prorhinotermes simplex* Hag.)
　 6. The eastern subterranean termite (*Reticulitermes flavipes* Kol.)
　 7. The southwestern soldierless termite (*Anoplotermes fumosus* Hag.)
　 8. The southwestern tube-forming desert termite (*Amitermes tubi-*
　 formans Buck.)
　 9. A nasutiform American termite (*Nasutitermes pilifrons* Holmg.)
　 Drawn by Thompson. Greatly enlarged.

large and extend them as the colony increases. Worker termites live underground, within the wood or in shelter tubes; they are usually in most species blind, and shun the light, and as a result are rarely seen. No workers are present in colonies of the more primitive termites, but the young or nymphs perform similar duties. Among the higher, more specialized termites, they may be polymorphic or of more than one type in the same species.

In view of the facts that workers do not occur among the lower, more primitive termites, and that the soldiers pass through a worker-like stage to maturity, Dr. A. E. Emerson of the University of Chicago has proposed the theory that the worker evolved from the soldier caste.

Among ants the workers are only of the female sex and they may sometimes be fertile. Termite workers are of both sexes and are never fertile; forms with wing pads or buds do not occur.

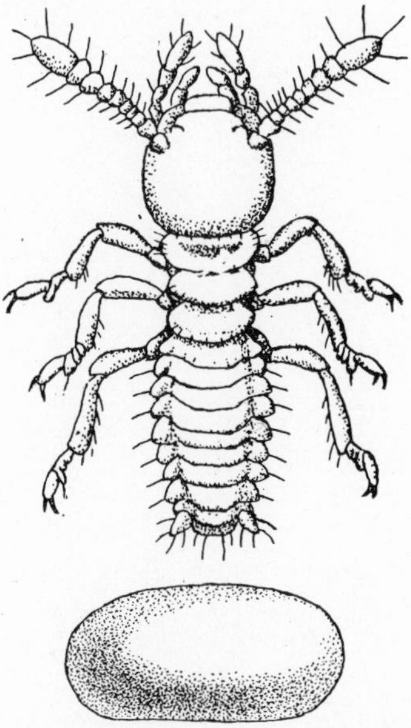

FIG. 11. Young or recently hatched nymph of our common eastern subterranean termite (*Reticulitermes flavipes* Kol.). Natural size, $\frac{1}{25}$ of an inch; the egg from which it hatched has a natural size of $\frac{1}{50}$ of an inch.

THE SOLDIERS. Like the workers, the soldiers are potentially both males and females, but are sterile and hence really neuters, since their reproductive organs are either incomplete or never mature. Hence, they too can never reproduce their kind. The form of the termite soldier differs much more greatly from the worker than is the case among the ants. Soldiers are large-headed forms, with large jaws or mandibles, only useful for defense and of no avail for cutting wood either for food or shelter. In addition to jaws, the soldiers may be armed with processes on the head, and with spines on the thorax or on the legs.

During a molt, early in the development of the soldier nymph, it changes from a form with saw-toothed mandibles to one where the mandibles have no marginal teeth, with the exception of

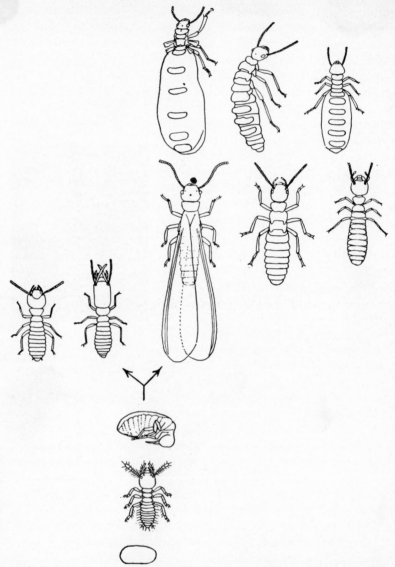

Fɪɢ. 12. Chart representing in diagrammatic form the development or life history of our common eastern subterranean termite (*Reticulitermes flavipes* Kol.) from the egg to the post-adult, showing two off-shoots, namely, the *sterile* soldier and the worker castes (left) and the three *fertile* reproductive forms (right). Enlarged.

rudiments at the bases of the mandibles. Gradually in later molts the round, worker-like head and the curved form of the mandibles change to the elongate, parallel-sided, soldier-like head, and the mandibles become sabre-like (fig. 14B).

While soldiers with jaws vary as to their fighting abilities, as a rule they are only effective in breaches, where their soft bodies are protected from rear or flank attack by enemy raiders. In some termites, the workers appear to be equally as effective warriors as the soldiers. While the bites of our native termites can not ordinarily be felt by man, workers and soldiers of tropical species can cause great annoyance and inconvenience to an observer studying their nests.

FIG. 13. A nymph of *Reticulitermes flavipes* Kol. in the resting or quiescent stage. Greatly enlarged.

When collecting in the Bahama Islands in 1922 during my first visit to the tropics, I was considerably surprised to find biting workers. A nasutiform termite built large carton nests on trees: some were as long as eight feet, and were three feet wide. When I searched these nests for termite guests, workers crawled all over me, stopping to bite now and then. I usually took back to the hotel many dead specimens and a few living and still biting termites in my clothes.

My first day's collecting in Panama in February, 1924, was scientifically productive, but rather hard on me personally. After a fairly inactive winter, I was " soft " and out of condition, so I became nearly exhausted struggling in the hot sun up and under the dense tangle of felled trees and brush of a recent clearing for a banana plantation to reach a patch of jungle. Here the collecting was excellent and I found a new variety of *Peripatus*, a worm-like creature close to the ancestral form of insects. I was also fortunate in rediscovering a " powder-post " termite recorded from Panama, but with no definite locality record, by Dudley and Beaumont during the latter part of the nineteenth century.

Not satisfied, finally emerging from the forest growth, I spied an elongate inverted cone-like carton nest in an isolated tree growing in a pasture. I had never before seen a nest like this, so I started up the tree. A brier-like vine growing on the trunk penetrated my skin and when half way up a small nest of wasps (*Polistes* sp.) was disturbed; the wasps stung me viciously. I

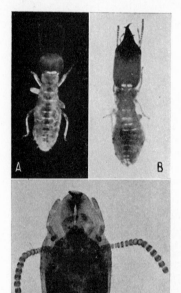

FIG. 14. A. Mature worker and B. soldier of *R. flavipes,* enlarged slightly over 6 times. C. View of the head of a soldier in a development stage between the worker-like form and the sabre-toothed mandible type. Enlarged 16 times.

fell down from the tree. Still determined, I knocked down the cone-like nest with a branch and broke into it. Out swarmed legions of a tropical ant (*Azteca* sp.), which soon covered me, biting viciously. I had expected to find termites in this nest. Chagrined, I turned away just in time to see a bull charging towards me. I fled and climbed the fence. Covered with young or seed ticks which were boring into my skin, and itching with " chigger " or red bug bites, I called it a day.

In the defense of the nest, there is cooperation between the workers and the soldiers. At the time of the swarm or colonizing flight of the winged adults, soldiers and workers line up at the exits or openings in the nests, head pointing outward (fig. 15). When the nests are damaged, there will be a similar battle array at the points where the breaks are. At these times of disturbance and alarm, great excitement is evidenced by both neuter castes, especially if the reproductive adults are nearby and appear to be endangered. Individuals go through the peculiar, more or less synchronous jerky or convulsive movements of the whole body that are supposed to be a method of communication through the substratum. Termites appear to be rather sensitive to vibrations. This same movement may be exhibited by some of the insect inquilines or guests in the nests of termites.

In other termites with mandibles or jaws, the head is developed or fitted for blocking passageways, as in species of *Cryptotermes*, the " powder-post " termites.

In some species, the soldiers have a short or long tube or nasus projecting from the front of the head (Plate I, fig. b) , the opening of the frontal gland, from which exudes or is expelled for a distance of an inch or less a sticky, semi-liquid, acidulous secretion, which may coagulate into a white waxy-appearing mass. This " glue " is discharged on the insects raiding the colony, which are usually ants.   In the case of ants, termites usually aim at or touch the petiole or pedicle, a thin stalk connecting the

FIG. 15.   Earth-like carton shelter showing openings in which workers and soldiers of *R. flavipes* stand guard during the swarm.

head and body.   This so thoroughly gums the ant together that it is rendered *hors de combat*.   Very evidently this " chemical warfare " is much more effective than fighting with the jaws.

This frontal gland, sometimes merely an opening on the front of the head, but often projected into a " nasus " or nose-like beak, has developed from the third or median simple eye or ocellus.   From the primitive soldier with biting jaws (Plate I, fig. a) have developed soldiers with both functional jaws and frontal gland (Plate I, figs. c, d) , and more specialized forms in which the mandibles are absent or vestigial and the gland only functional (Plate I, fig. b) .

Species of *Rhinotermes* occurring in tropical America and related to our North American subterranean termites in the genus

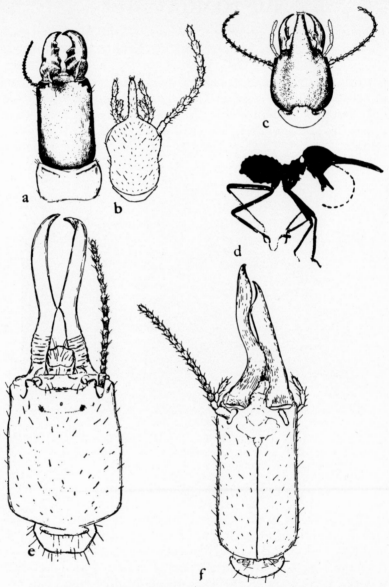

PLATE I. Soldier termites from the American tropics with different types of defense organs. a. Head of a primitive Kalotermitid with biting jaws only. b. Head of a nasutiform termite with nasus for "chemical warfare" or gland defense. c. Head of *Armitermes intermedius* Sny. with both jaws and tube or gland defense. d. Soldier of *Armitermes (Rhynchotermes) perarmatus* Sny., a very odd Panamanian termite with both jaws and elongate exudate defense tube. e. and f. Heads of soldiers with jaws unsuited for biting but adapted for flipping.

Reticulitermes have dimorphic soldiers, or soldiers of two types. The large or " major " soldier has long, toothed mandibles, but also is specialized for " chemical warfare ". The labrum or upper lip is prolonged into a long trough, which directs the flow of a secretion toxic to ants. The small or " minor " soldier has only vestigial mandibles and also has an elongate, trough-like upper lip, and is adapted for chemical warfare as is the major soldier.

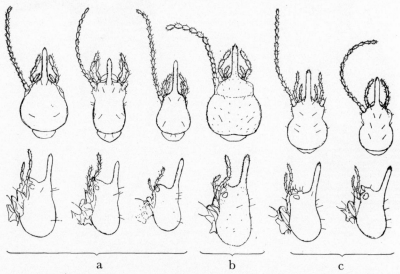

a   b   c

FIG. 16. Dorsal and side views of heads of nasutiform termites to show polymorphism or difference in form of soldiers of the same species.
  a. Three types of soldier present, major, intermediate, and minor.
  b. One type of soldier only present.
  c. Two types of soldier present.

The condition in the genus *Armitermes* of tropical America may be considered as transitional or intermediate in the progress of the evolution of this highly specialized gland and in the later reduction or regressive development of the jaws. In some species of *Armitermes,* the jaws are more dominant than the frontal gland, and in other the reverse is the case.

Where the frontal gland is dominant, the soldiers are nasutiform or nasutes, veritable Cyrano de Bergeracs!

In other termites, the jaws are asymmetrical and sometimes twisted or goat-like; they are not adapted for biting, but are used in defense by snapping or leaping (Plate I, figs. e, f) , or are used in signaling.

Both mandibulate soldiers (those with jaws) and the nasutiform type may be polymorphic or of several different types (three at most) in the same species (fig. 16) . None of these varied types of soldiers are capable of feeding themselves on wood or vegetation. They must be fed by the workers, as are the young and reproductive forms, on specially predigested or " conditioned " food. Indeed, in one genus (*Anoplotermes*) , a specialized, highly developed termite, the soldier caste has been lost. During evolutionary development, of course, there are both losses and gains to be observed in tracing the descent of living termites.

" Intermediate " forms, or individuals having characters of two castes, are rather rare among termites. It is true that among the colonizing, reproductive types such intermediate forms or " intercastes ", ranging from wingless or apterous forms to macropterous forms (forms with long wing pads) , are not uncommon. But when we consider the sterile soldier and worker castes, intermediates are very rare.

FIG. 17. Head and thorax of the soldier of a primitive termite (*Kalotermes occidentis* Walk.) to show the presence of wing pads.

In colonies of *Kalotermes occidentis* Walker, of Arizona and western Mexico, a very primitive termite and the largest known member of *Kalotermes,* all soldiers have rudimentary wing pads or traces of wings (fig. 17) , whereas among most other primitive termites short wing pads are only occasionally found on a small proportion of the soldiers of the colony. These soldiers are not fertile, but are merely reversions to the ancestral winged termite of the days when there were no sterile workers or soldiers.

Where fertile soldier-like forms do occur, as in species of the primitive *Zoötermopsis* of the Pacific Coast of North America and *Archotermopsis* of Northern India, the form of the soldier is not normal, and the creature may be considered an intermediate between the ancestral winged sexual adult and the normal sterile soldier (fig. 18). None of the higher, more specialized termites have soldiers with wing pads or egg-laying soldier-like forms; and no fertile workers of any termite have as yet been discovered.

Among the termites classified between the primitive and the higher termites, such as our common genus *Reticulitermes* of North America and the north temperate regions of the world, a rare abnormality has been found. In the species *tibialis* Banks of western United States a male half-worker, half-soldier form was found over sixteen years ago near Missoula, Montana. The head has the characteristic color of the soldier caste and is slightly longer than the head of the worker. The mandibles and the labrum or upper lip are typically worker-like, but are extended as in the soldier. This form may merely be a worker of abnormal development, or it may be an intermediate between the worker and soldier castes.

The soldier develops from a worker-like form during a quiescent stage to the soldier-like form, thereby in the development of the individual from nymph to adult, or "ontogeny", expressing the "phylogeny" or history of the origin of the worker caste. This is in line with Dr. Emerson's theory that the

FIG. 18. Intermediate soldier-sexual form of a native rotten wood termite *Zoötermopsis nevadensis* Hag.

worker is an offshoot from the soldier. In other words, in the course of the development of an individual soldier, the same stages are passed through that the worker caste passed through in its development, long ago, from the soldier caste. If something untoward happens during this transformation, abnormalities or intercastes may be produced; there may be an arrested development and a partially developed form may result.

Recently I found a very definite intermediate soldier-worker form in a vial among a small collection of termites sent to me for identification. This intermediate soldier-worker form has the color of the soldier, but has a shorter nasus than the soldier and has worker-like saw-toothed mandibles. Other differences are that this intermediate has fourteen segments to the antennae like the worker, whereas the soldier has only thirteen. The third segment is merely longer than either the second or the third, whereas in the soldier the third segment is nearly as long as the second and third segments together. In general, this form is more worker-like than soldier-like (fig. 19).

A comparison may be made of the phylogeny of the fertile and sterile termite castes, as evidenced in their ontogeny (or individual development or evolution), with the phylogeny of the fertile and sterile portions of a plant. In the white, sweet-scented water lily (*Nymphaea odorata*) some of the anthers have been transformed into petals; all gradations between an-

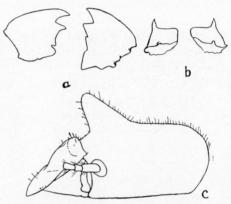

FIG. 19.   a. Dorsal view of mandibles of worker and soldier-worker intermediate of a Brazilian nasutiform termite (*Nasutitermes* (*N.*) *myersi* Sny.). b. Dorsal view of mandibles of a soldier. c. Lateral view of head of a soldier-worker intermediate. Enlarged 27 times.

ther and petal may be seen in a single flower. These petals may be less important functionally than the anthers, yet each serves a purpose. The sterile soldier termites — more highly specialized than the workers — are less important functionally than the workers, and both are less necessary than the fertile forms from which they have developed. Yet they all serve needs in the colony life.

THE REPRODUCTIVE ADULTS. The small-headed forms develop into nymphs of the three types of sexual, colonizing, reproductive adults; namely, the form with the long wing pads, or macropterous nymphs, that with the short wing pads, or brachypterous nymphs, and the type with no traces of wings at all, the apterous nymphs.

The form with the long wing pads (fig. 20), which are opaque at maturity and show traces of wing venation, develops, after a series of molts and quiescent stages, into the winged adult. This growth to the mature, long winged or macropterous adult extends over a period of two years. These brownish or blackish, elongate, slender, colonizing, sexual adults with long wings, unlike the other forms, have functional eyes, and their bodies are able to endure full sunlight. These migratory males and females appear normally once a year during a short period in large

FIG. 20. Mature nymphs of the first form reproductive adults (with long wing pads) and the second form (with short wing pads) of our common eastern subterranean termite. Greatly enlarged.

numbers in a " swarm " to establish new colonies; in continental United States this period is usually in the spring or autumn.

Except in the matter of coloring, the nymphs with the short wing pads in general resemble the brachypterous, sexual, colonizing adult. This is a caste with similar functions to those of the macropterous reproductive adult. In well-established parent colonies of *Reticulitermes* large numbers of nymphs with short wing pads seasonally appear each year. They mature at the same time as the winged adults, but before the swarm, and pass through similar molts during quiescent stages of relatively short duration.

Even as immature nymphs, the brachypterous forms are more active than the macropterous nymphs. Yet their body structure is grosser in form. Both sexes of these two types of nymphs have " stylets " or genital appendices on the ventral surface of the ninth abdominal segment (fig. 21a). At the final molt, the females (in *Reticulitermes*) of the macropterous, brachypterous, and apterous types lose these stylets, an immature character in the female; hence they are now really adults. In the apterous re-

Fig. 21. Winged adult of *R. flavipes*.

productive types of the more primitive *Archotermopsis* and *Zoötermopsis* these stylets are not lost in the female. They are an aid in sex determination in biological studies and breeding work. For many years the writer had noted in certain colonies of species of *Reticulitermes* that where there were numerous eggs and recently hatched young it was impossible to find any enlarged reproductive form. Nevertheless, in these colonies, nymphs worker-like in form but with creamy white abdomens often occurred. It was then discovered that these were young "apterous" reproductive forms. When mature, they attain a partial, very slight coloring. Stylets are present, which are lost in the mature female.

Due to the fact that the eggs are not all laid at the same time, and hatch at different times, there is an overlapping in development. Hence, in well-established colonies, there are usually to be found nymphs of all three reproductive types, the macropterous and brachypterous being common, the apterous form more rare. The three types all mature at approximately the same time.

We thus see that the termite colony is a complex association of castes, all of which may be useful either in maintaining the colony or in founding new colonies. These different forms have all developed from eggs and young that looked alike, at least externally. The mature macropterous reproductive adults, de-

Female   Male

FIG. 21a. A comparison of the ventral abdominal segments of the male and female of the winged adult. *R. flavipes*. Greatly enlarged.

veloped by a post-adult growth from deälated adults, were until fairly recently (1909) thought to be very rare in colonies. In searching for the cell which contains the king and queen, it must be remembered that the location depends upon the species and habits of the termite, the geographical locality, the climate, and the season of the year; also it must not be forgotten that one may encounter any one of three different reproductive types.

The commonest type in the case of *Reticulitermes flavipes* Kol. of eastern United States appears to be the macropterous form. The winged or macropterous adults for the sake of convenience are hereafter also to be called first form adults; the brachypterous adults, those of the second form; and the apterous type, third form adults. The first form have a darker color to the body segments than the other two forms, wing stubs, and have both simple and compound eyes. Queens of this type reach the greatest dimensions, becoming as large as 16.5mm ($\frac{3}{4}$ of an inch) in length and 4.5mm ($\frac{1}{4}$ of an inch) in width, or thirty times the size of a worker (which is 4.5mm in length) by volumetric displacement. The largest queens, those with markedly enlarged abdomens (physogastric queens), occur among species of *Termes* from Africa. In the collection of the United States National Museum such queens are 2400 times the volume of their workers.

The macropterous type or first form is apparently the parent of the other reproductive forms as well as of the worker and soldier castes.

Another type of reproductive adult fairly common in colonies of species of *Reticulitermes* is the brachypterous or second form with short wing pads. Unlike the first form adult, this type has but little color, which is usually of a pale straw-yellow or graybrown. This color is suggestive of a subterranean habit and more complete seclusion from light. The compound eyes are reduced in size and have a pale color.

Probably only the first form adults are able to perceive images; the other reproductive types may be able to perceive light and direction by means of their simple eyes or ocelli and their reduced compound eyes.

In general the first form adults are very slender, and everything has been sacrificed for lightness of body, a primary necessity for the colonizing flight. Even most of the intestinal protozoa are lost, before the swarm. The second form adults have a grosser structure; they are heavier and are not intended for flight. At the time of their maturity, just before the swarming of the winged adults, the sex glands of the second form adults are ready to function; this is not the case with the first form. At this time the adults of the second form also have lost their intestinal protozoa. Physogastric second form or brachypterous queens attain a length of $\frac{1}{2}$ inch; often the abdomen has an irregular, lumpy appearance. They are either congregated in one large chamber or suitably distributed in many small chambers, in the ratio of many females to few brachypterous males; four to one is a common occurrence, or perhaps as many as 126 females to 113 males. This form, unlike the normally monogamous first form adult, is polygamous. The males have the abdomens compressed laterally, which gives them the appearance of having a narrow, ridged back.

Sometimes a male of the first form, a macropterous king, will be associated with a group of sixteen or seventeen wingless or third form queens, or even a larger number of brachypterous females or second form queens. Some accident has happened to the normal queen of his own type. With her loss " complementary " females have replaced the original queen of the macropterous type. The young of such replacement forms occur in colonies, and, after a period of development, are ready to substitute.

Just before the swarm or colonizing flight takes place, brachypterous or second form adults (as well as apterous adults) apparently disappear from parent colonies where they have been present in large numbers. What happens to them? Are they killed by the workers, on whom they now depend for food, since they have lost their intestinal protozoa? They are no longer needed in the parent colony. Or do they migrate to form new colonies?

But little is known of the habits of the second or third form reproductive adults and how they establish new colonies, which some of them do. Possibly the normal habit is for some of them to migrate with workers and soldiers through subterranean passages and thus establish new colonies. These colonizing reproductive adults may be impelled to leave the parent colony by the same stimuli as the winged adults.

Sometimes brachypterous adults of both sexes in species of *Reticulitermes* engage in a short false flight or attempt at flight, the so-called " pseudo-flight ", at the same time that the winged adults are swarming. They come out of the parent colony into the full sunlight, and run about, or climb to slight elevations as do the winged, and make slight short jumps or flips into the air — as do also the deälated, formerly winged adults, after they have lost their wings. Often they fall over backwards.

Possibly this activity is a manifestation of or a reversion to the ancestral habit of swarming, or colonization by flight. In the absence of wings they can only run about and flip themselves into the air.

Or, if this is not a reversion to the ancestral winged type, perhaps it goes back still farther to the fossil Palaeodictyoptera, or oldest known insects, which in addition to primitive wings had lobes on the sides of the prothorax, which look like undeveloped

wings. If wings were evolved from such flaps on the meso-
thorax and meta-thorax, there was a time when ancient insects
could not fly. Possibly they could glide from heights as do certain animals to-day, such as flying squirrels. This might explain
second form adults climbing to heights and jerking themselves
into the air. Certain of the more primitive termites (*Kalotermes*) today have these prothoracic lobes in the nymphal
stage.

It is more probable that second form adults normally leave
with workers and soldiers by subterranean passages, since these
forms must be fed by the workers in order to survive. This
" pseudo-flight " only occasionally occurs in colonies and probably is a reversion manifested only by a few adults.

According to Cleveland, in *Zoötermopsis,* a more primitive
termite, the intestinal protozoa are never entirely lost, but are
greatly diminished. Here, no workers exist, but the duties of
the workers are performed by the young or nymphs. In *Zoötermopsis,* wingless or apterous adults in artificial colonies have
been observed in similar pseudo-flight movements.

There is proof that the second form reproductive adults may
breed true to type and never produce winged adults, but only
nymphs of their own type and workers and soldiers. In artificial
colonies, maintained for many years, neither winged reproductive adults nor third form reproductive adults have been produced in colonies where the parent adults were second form.

A rarer type of reproductive adult is the apterous, third form
or worker-like adult. No wings or wing pads are present; there
is but little color to the body, and there are only traces of eyes,
no doubt because of its wholly subterranean mode of life. The
general appearance and shape of the apterous queens is less gross
and more closely resembles the first form type in general than
does the second. As in the second form adults, males of corresponding form occur with the queens, a few kings to many
queens; sometimes a ratio of 16 to 1. The largest third form
queen found in species of *Reticulitermes* is only 9mm (about
$\frac{1}{3}$ of an inch) in length.

The third form colonizing reproductive adult probably is
able to establish new colonies in the same manner as the second
form adults, leaving the parent colony with workers and soldiers
by subterranean galleries. Apparently this form likewise breeds

true to type, for in many years of observation in artificial colonies they have never produced winged adults.

While males of the higher and intermediately classified termites are normally monogamous, in the more primitive termites they are more often polygamous; a few males are associated with many females.

"INTERMEDIATE" REPRODUCTIVE FORMS. Rather few "intermediate" reproductive forms have been found among termites. The late Father Odenbach discovered a physogastric, egg-laying queen of *Reticulitermes flavipes* Kol., with long, well-developed wing pads, as in the first form nymph. A queen which in respect to the wing pads is an intermediate between the first and second form nymphs was discovered in Italy by B. Grassi in the species *Reticulitermes lucifugus* of Mediterranean Europe. Similar forms have been found among our native species of *Reticulitermes*.

In species of the more primitive *Zoötermopsis* of the Pacific Coast, there is a larger series of intermediates between the apterous or third form and normal second form adults; these forms are of more common occurrence than among species of *Reticulitermes*.

In species of the lower termites *Zoötermopsis* and *Kalotermes* the third form reproductive adults have marked color to the body and slight color to the reduced compound eyes, unlike *Reticulitermes*. But in species of the less primitive *Rhinotermes* and *Prorhinotermes* the body alone is colored. This is probably due to the fact that the former species live above ground or are non-subterranean, while all of the latter species except in *Prorhinotermes* are subterranean.

Vestigial, shorter wing pads, or buds, are noticeable in reproductive adults of *Zoötermopsis*, and typical second form adults are rare; and in *Prorhinotermes* they are entirely absent. In North American species of *Kalotermes,* third form adults with definite color to the body and slight color to the reduced compound eyes are rare, but second form adults are not uncommon.

Among the more specialized termites in the highest family (the Termitidae), second form reproductive adults with incompletely colored body and eyes are common and even "intermediates" or intercastes have been found. However, no third form or reproductive adults without traces of wings have been discovered. I have found second form reproductive adults in North American species of *Gnathamitermes,* one of the specialized groups of desert termites.

In the tropics, second form reproductive adults are especially common among species of *Armitermes, Nasutitermes,* and *Microcerotermes,* all highly specialized groups. In a species of *Microcerotermes* from the Solomon Islands, in the South Seas, have been found many second form reproductive adults with wing pads or buds varying in length from normal to as long as those in first form nymphs; indeed they represented a well-graded series of intermediates between these two types.

There is a parallelism between the castes and the various less common, abnormal " intermediates " of termites and Mendelian " segregants ", in which there is a splitting up of complex parental hereditary material into many simpler types of off-spring or segregants. The origin of castes can be explained by no other theory of evolution and there is no positive proof that special, qualitative feeding can determine the castes. Indeed, there is much evidence to disprove the explanation of origin of castes by immediate environment, such as food.

There are no fertile workers or soldiers among termites; those fertile soldiers reported to occur in the primitive termites *Archotermopsis* and *Zoötermopsis* are believed to be " intermediate " reproductive forms.

" Parthenogenesis " (virgin birth) does not occur among the termites as it does in some groups of insects. Also, apparently neither " paedogenesis " nor true " neoteny " or birth by individuals of nymphal aspect exists in termites. " Hermaphroditism " or self-fertilization also does not occur among termites, for no such biological monstrosities as " gynandromorphs " or part male and part female individuals occur; they are found among ants, where, however, they do not function. See the glossary for a more detailed account of these interesting forms of reproduction.

In fact, while many peculiar forms of reproduction occur among the invertebrates they appear to be lacking among the termites, which do, however, have a large number of reproductive types. More careful research work is needed on the castes, their stability or plasticity and their origin before we can be more definite.

CHAPTER III

THE COLONIZING FLIGHT

UNUSUAL flights of any insects always attract the attention of even the most unobservant person. Such flights are usually mating or marriage flights, where the male seeks out the female and often fertilizes her in mid-air; but in the case of termites it is simply a colonizing flight. Of course the strongest fliers and the most fit are surest of securing mates. The observer is often struck with awe at the bounty of nature in producing insects in such enormous numbers.

One type of such nuptial flights has been observed but by few white men, since it occurs in the realm of the Seminole Indians, in localities until recently somewhat inaccessible. I well recall my first vivid impressions of a remarkable flight of large gadflies or horse flies.

Two figures are slowly moving along a path in a dense hammock in the Lower Everglades of Florida, stopping now and then, tensely listening. It is 4 A.M. and early spring, and the stars are still shining, especially the bright morning star, but dawn is tinting the east, the faint light outlining the jungle growth overtopped by majestic feathery royal palms. Suddenly a barred owl, disappointed in a lonely vigil for frogs, begins a dismal hooting; as we approach it flies from a live oak limb.

Finally a faint buzzing is heard, which gradually increases to a dull roar; thousands of large flies can be seen above the tree tops steadily hovering or suddenly darting to and fro. This is the early morning flight of the large gadfly — *Tabanus americanus* Forster. After a short period the loud buzzing gradually diminishes in volume, and only a few low-hovering flies remain. At the end of about fifteen minutes the flight is entirely over for the day.

This peculiar flight is what we have come out to observe and note. In the early morning light a more hasty return to camp is made. A large bull alligator near his wallow in a slough in

the Everglades is loudly roaring. Birds are beginning to call
and soon the sun will rise across the sawgrass prairie.

Particularly striking as an example of the lavishness of nature
is the midsummer flight of an ant (*Lasius niger* L., var. *americanus* Emery) , which I have frequently seen along the seacoast
of southern Virginia. Swarming by myriads, the winged ants are
yearly blown out to sea. Later they are washed up by the waves
on the sandy beach in black windrows, miles in length. Here
they are fed upon by " fiddler crabs ", which greedily stuff them
into their mouths with both claws.

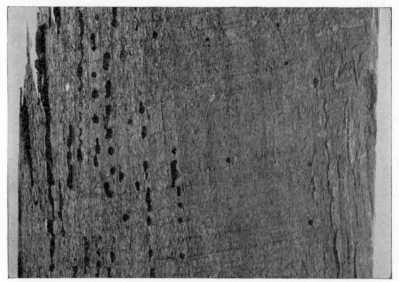

FIG. 22. Exit holes in wood of winged adults of our common subterranean
termite.

In contrast with such nuptial flights, the flights of termites
are simply for the purpose of founding new colonies. They
are, therefore, known as colonizing flights.

There is almost an element of magic attendant upon a swarm
of termites, especially those large tropical species which fly in
enormous numbers. While there has been much and long
preparation for the swarm within the nest, the outward mani-
festations are of striking suddenness.

Apertures are opened in the ground, in wood (fig. 22) , or in
the earth-like chimneys (fig. 15) built up by the workers. From

the exits the air becomes alive with fluttering winged hordes of termites. Soldiers and workers guard the emergence holes before, during, and after the flight.

After the departure of the first form adults, the exit holes are closed from within by the workers and all trace of life disappears as suddenly as it appeared. The only evidence remaining that a flight has taken place is in the discarded wings lying on the ground.

This swarm is the annual colonizing and dispersal flight of the winged male and female termites. The sexes are represented in approximately equal numbers. Actual counts of the males and females during swarms both in this country and in the tropics have determined this as fact.

Aborigines in Africa often surround mound nests of termites before the swarm with broad leaves in order to collect them in large quantities for food; they are greatly prized as delicacies. Children of East African natives make rhythmic noises by hammering with sticks upon wood, producing sounds as of pattering rain to lure termites to swarm into traps. Tropical termites often swarm only after rainfall.

While most termites are but poor fliers, there are records of some termites flying or being carried by the wind several miles. In airplane surveys made by the United States Bureau of Entomology at Tallulah, Louisiana, to determine at what heights various insects fly or are blown, termites were collected. Winged adults of the subterranean *Reticulitermes virginicus* Banks were caught at altitudes of 2000 and 3000 feet. At 2000 feet, the wind velocity was 24 miles per hour, while on the ground it was only 11 miles per hour. At 3000 feet, the wind was blowing at 10 miles per hour, but only 6 miles per hour on the ground.

The larger, more primitive termites have a longer, stronger flight than intermediate or higher termites. They emerge from parent colonies in smaller numbers and at more irregular intervals, usually at night. The more specialized termites are restricted annually to a few weak flights, made, however, in enormous numbers; the first flight usually contains the largest number of individuals, but other flights from the same colony may appear over a period of a month.

The line of weakness or suture where the wing is attached to the base, and where it breaks off, the so-called humeral suture, is well defined in the higher termites. These termites some- times lose one or both wings in mid-air and then drop in spirals to earth like a pine or maple tree seed, under the control of air currents.

The lower termites are forced to pry off their wings, since the suture is but poorly defined. Their antics in attempting to obtain advantage of leverage in prying off their wings are very amusing. The wings are pressed against a stone, a piece of wood, or any other available object. Among some of the primi- tive roaches which are subsocial in habit and burrow in wood this same suture occurs. Termites never bite off their wings.

Possibly there is some cross-fertilization by the intermingling of individuals from different colonies, thus preventing inbreed- ing. Usually, individuals from the same colony mate, although there is synchronous flight from many different, widely separated colonies of the same kind of termite (species of *Reticulitermes*). They emerge at the same time from colonies in logs, stumps, or the ground, or from infested buildings in the same general locality — such as an entire township or a whole village.

Usually the winged adults appear on a warm, sunny spring morning. Different species of *Reticulitermes* swarm at dif- ferent times; there is also a difference in the time of swarming due to geographical locality and to variations in seasons. The flights are, however, in the spring or autumn or at both times. Near Washington, D. C., the species which swarms earliest (*flavipes*) appears from outdoor colonies during the last of April or first of May. Another species (*virginicus*) swarms in the first part of June, and a late flying species (*hageni*) does not appear until July or August.

By proceeding farther north (within the range of the occur- rence of the termite), or going to a higher altitude, one finds the swarming times to be later.

Because of the short, weak flight of most termites, the swarm does not result in a very rapid, wide dispersal or aid in the diffusion of the species. However, over a period of time there may be considerable distribution. There seems to be no regu- lar formation to the flight, and the direction depends upon the wind.

This synchronous or simultaneous swarming of termites is

one of the rhythmic activities in the life of the colony which is but little understood. The winged adults have been in the colony for some time previous to the swarm, apparently ready for the flight; indeed, they can be induced to fly earlier by disturbing the colony. What are the stimuli, internal or external or both, which impel them to start to fly from these different colonies all at the same time? The stimulus is probably a combination of favorable temperature and humidity conditions, and these factors, particularly humidity, govern the time of flight.

Because their sex glands are still immature, winged termites are not ready for sexual mating at the time of the flight. Everything has been sacrificed to attain lightness. Even most of the intestinal protozoa have been lost before the swarm.

After this vacillating flight, the winged termites fall on the ground or alight and then pry off their wings. Normally, only after losing their wings (becoming deälated) are the males and females attracted to each other. This is not the case, however, among some of the primitive termites, which sometimes do not lose or shed their wings until within the cell in wood where the young colony is to be reared; the sex attraction occurs immediately after the flight.

COURTSHIP AND PAIRING

Few indeed are the deälated adults that are able to escape the hordes of greedy predatory enemies which are attracted in large numbers to the meal offered by the swarming insects. So many of the helpless termites are gulped down or carried off that it does not seem possible that any could survive.

The surviving deälates pair off in couples, the male closely and tirelessly following the female, with head close to her abdomen and his feelers or antennae in constant touch with her. This rather rapid pursuit or running about after the female occurs for some time after the swarm and is called " amatory procedure ". Sometimes two or more males will follow in file after the same female. The fact that the female when alone runs about rather rapidly with her abdomen raised in the air indicates that there is an odor related to sex present. Males are stimulated and excited by such actions and are attracted to these females, with whom they pair as described above but do not as yet mate sexually.

There is probably, in addition to odor, a contact stimulus between the sexes which leads to this close association; the male continuously strokes the abdomen of the female with his feelers.

THE FOUNDING OF NEW COLONIES

Together males and females found a new colony by excavating a shallow cell in the earth, in the earth under wood or other vegetation, or in crevices or under bark in moist wood. The very small percentage of deälates surviving the host of animal life preying on the swarming adults now have to meet and overcome the hazards of unfavorable conditions of environment such as character of soil, temperature, moisture, absence of food.

Some termites, inhabiting hot arid areas, could not thus become established in the hard, caked, dry soil until after it had been softened by rain; in consequence they do not swarm until after rainfall. Neither do certain " powder-post " or " house termites " which live in very dry wood. So the softening of the ground is the effect of rainfall and the real cause of the swarm is not the rainfall in itself.

No matter what happens, winged colonizing adults never return to the parent colony, and probably no colonizing form ever returns to the original colony.

TROPISMS OR INSTINCTIVE REACTION TENDENCIES

We cannot infer that termites have consciousness: they merely respond to stimuli, which may be either external, internal, or both. Forms of behavior resulting from stimuli are called tropisms; collectively, tropisms become an instinct.

Termites (species of *Reticulitermes*) within a few hours on a bright, sunny morning in spring may pass through a series of such tropisms. First, at the beginning of the swarm, the first form and sometimes even the second form sexual adults cease to shun the light and become phototropic; they fly and crawl about in the bright sunlight, a direct reversal of the pre-swarming behavior. The fact that many termites fly at dusk or at night, often after rainfall, may indicate that the principal stimulus is an exact necessary condition of temperature and moisture. Nevertheless, there is a complete reversal in behavior.

Secondly, several observers have noticed that before the flight the winged adults climb on an elevated object to some height, such as upon brush, a stump, or grass stems. Even the second form or brachypterous reproductive adults climb to elevations, and although they cannot fly, they engage in a " pseudo-flight ", or attempt to fly by jerking themselves up into the air for short distances. Sometimes the workers construct " chimneys " or towers of earth and excreta before the flight. This behavior has been termed " negative geotropism ", or turning away from the earth, by Dr. A. E. Emerson of the University of Chicago. Students of the habits of termites have for many years sought to discover the actual trigger which stimulates or sets off the swarm.

Thirdly, after the flight both the first and second form adults become " actively thigmotropic ", or desirous of coming in contact with some object. They seem impelled to get under something. They also become light-shunning, as they were before the swarm, directly reversing behavior only recently attained. For only a short period do we find these subterranean termites in the sunlight, or, in the case of the night-flying termites, attracted to artificial lights.

From now on, these colonizing termites lead a cloistered life. They have renounced forever light and the outside world. They remain underground or within wood or shelter tubes, shun light, or the lack of humidity of the outdoors, and dig in for their long undercover life within earth or wood. Their life in the light and open has indeed been ephemeral! The shelter tubes are probably "air conditioned " tunnels to conserve humidity rather than merely for protection against ants or sunlight.

THE SENSE ORGANS

This leads us to wonder about perception and how termites receive impulses or stimuli. But little is known of the sense organs of termites and the reactions of these insects to various stimuli. Body odors, as well as odors related to sex and to nest, certainly appear to have an influence on the activities of the termite colony. The nest odor is of a peculiar, distinctive acrid or musty nature.

When specimens of eastern subterranean termites are placed in a jar containing a colony of rotten wood termites from the Pacific Coast, the host termites recognize these foreign insects — probably by difference in odor — and eventually kill the invaders.   The progress of the chase and kill is very slow and the larger host termites appear awkward in their efforts to bite and kill their smaller but quicker moving cousins.   Finally, more or less by sheer numbers and accident, they corner and exter-

Fig. 23.   Earth-like shelter tubes of a native subterranean termite run straight from the earth over a wall to wood.

minate the enemy.   Usually death is slow and there is a gradual dismemberment.

After having been in the colony of the rotten wood termite from the Pacific Coast for a week, deälated adults of the southeastern subterranean termite still survived.   Apparently they had taken on the odor of the host termite and were no longer molested.   Previously, winged adults of this subterranean termite had been pursued and killed.   Fresh specimens placed in the colony at this time were immediately attacked.

Body odor, as well as contact stimuli, aid blind worker and soldier termites to maintain a single file formation outside of the main nest. This can be observed by watching termites under an upturned log or stone. Either one or the other of these stimuli, or possibly both, enables termites to run a straight course to a source of food (fig. 23) and might account for other activities, sometimes grouped under the heading of the mysterious " spirit of the colony ".

Termites have sense or "chordotonal organs ", or vibration receptors, located on the antennae, bristles, or at the base of the mandibles, and pores on the legs which possibly enable them to receive and respond to vibrations sent through the air. Or, much more probably, the sense organs located on the legs enable termites to receive stimuli sent through the earth or nest material, or through air pockets between nest material. May there not exist a system of wireless telegraphy, especially adapted to these blind insects?

Of course, the more or less synchronous, convulsive movements exhibited by the workers and soldiers, when alarmed, would appear to be a method of communication adapted to blind insects; no sound is produced, however, which is audible to man. Termite soldiers also strike their heads against wood and other nest material, thus making a noise.

Such sounds, amplified to crackling or rustling noises by nest material, which serves as a sounding board, are plainly audible to man's possibly duller or differently attuned perceptions. In fact, soldiers of a species of *Reticulitermes* in California striking their heads against the dry, dead flower stalks of a Spanish bayonet or agave in the desert region can be heard several feet away. Other types of soldier termites, which occur in the tropics, such as a species of *Mirotermes,* make audible clicking noises with their jaws.

It seems very probable that there is some correspondence between these sound-producing movements with accompanying noises and the sense organs. Termites appear to be very sensitive to vibrations; seldom are they found infesting railroad ties, over which there is frequent heavy traffic, or in the woodwork of mill or factory buildings in a vicinity where heavy machinery in motion would cause vibrations. Possible reasons are that vibration would not only interfere with termites' methods of com-

munication, but also, if heavy enough, would break off shelter
tubes.

FERTILIZATION

After fertilization, among comparable social insects, the ants
and bees, the male dies during the nuptial flight. The male
termite, on the other hand, helps to excavate the new nest or
cell, which in termites with permanent nests may be called the
" royal cell ". Both eat wood for food, and after the sex glands
have developed to maturity the bodies become slightly distended,
due to body fat and sexual maturity. It is about one week after
the swarm that copulation takes place and the female is fertilized.

It was formerly thought by some observers that it would be
impossible for the relatively small male or king to fertilize the
huge queen of some of the tropical termites. It was believed
that the eggs must be fertilized after they had been laid. Queens
of African termites (*Termes* sp.) are over four inches in length,
and an inch in width, and of about the same height, whereas the
male is only about three-fifths of an inch in length, less than
one-sixth of an inch in width, and an eighth of an inch in height.
By comparing the relative amounts of liquid which they dis-
place, when placed in a graduated vessel, such queens are found
to be 160 times the size of the king, and about 2400 times the size
of the worker! However, the male does not mount the female;
superimposition is *not* the manner of coition, as it is among
many insects. The sexes mate with the apices of the abdomens
opposed, as is the method among roaches and some other insects.

In species of *Reticulitermes,* the introduction to actual copulation is a lively play with the antennae and feet; the insects are
facing in opposite directions, the bodies curved together so as
to make a circle. The body is moved backward and forward,
hinging on the legs, and finally to both sides, as if the abdomens
were to be telescoped. The time of the connection is from one
to three minutes, during which the bodies remain closely appressed.

Dr. H. Heath of Stanford University states that among the
rotten wood termites or species of *Zoötermopsis* copulation lasts
for ten minutes.

Thereafter coition is repeated at irregular and shorter intervals, and the male continues to cohabit with the female for life.

RATE OF EGG LAYING

In species of *Reticulitermes,* egg laying begins about one and one-half months after the swarm. The eggs are laid singly, and from six to twelve constitute the first batch. They receive the same care from the workers — that is, they are groomed or licked and tended — that is later bestowed upon the young. The eggs are carried by the young parents or the workers into a favorable position in the nest where they are placed in clusters, often in the more outlying galleries where they will receive greater warmth.

In old, well-established colonies of our common subterranean termites of the eastern United States, egg laying takes place from April to October, the period of maximum egg production being during the warmer months. But in artificial colonies in the laboratory, or in infested heated buildings, egg laying may occur throughout the year. With the age of the colony, the rate of egg laying increases.

Tens of thousands of eggs are often found in large colonies of these subterranean termites, and, allowing for a period of incubation of ten days, the rate of egg laying must be rather rapid; the time taken in hatching, however, varies. The rate of egg laying also depends upon whether the parent reproductive forms are a single male and female or whether the male is polygamous; sometimes forty to one hundred reproductive adults of the second form are present in one colony.

None of our native termites have an egg laying rate approaching that of certain tropical kinds, where the huge egg laying machine called the queen, immobile and imprisoned with the king in a special, domed " royal cell ", may lay the enormous number of 80,000 eggs per day.

As with our common subterranean termites, the rate of egg laying by young and active queens in incipient colonies of dry-wood termites — species of *Kalotermes* — is but slow; only from six to twelve comprise the first batch. Among the rotten wood termites or the large species of *Zoötermopsis,* there is a slightly greater initial rate of egg laying, but the rate even here is not particularly rapid or great. With changing conditions in the nest, there are temporary shifts in the location of the eggs; and, of course, there are changes dependent upon the seasons.

Only in the case of one of our native powder-post termites
(*Cryptotermes cavifrons* Banks) of southern Florida have eggs
been found in anything resembling special cells.   In colonies of
this termite the eggs were observed to have been placed in small
separate pockets, among fluffy frass or wood particles.

INCUBATION

Before hatching, the eggs swell up perceptibly and increase
in size. While some eggs hatch about ten days after they are
laid, young of various sizes are always present in colonies, so the
eggs do not all hatch uniformly and a much longer time is taken
for the incubation of all the eggs.
The new colony is at first very
small, and even after the rearing
of the first brood of workers and
soldiers the increase in numbers
is not very rapid.   The first
brood which hatches develops, in
species *Reticulitermes*, mostly to
workers, with only one or two
soldiers.

FIG. 24.   " Conidia "   or   small
" cauliflowers " on   which termites in Java feed.   These are
developed from the thread-like
mycelium of the fungus, cultivated by the termites in their
gardens.

These first born of both castes
are smaller than the normal, mature individuals which develop
in old, long-established colonies.
The smaller size of these workers
and soldiers of the first brood may be explained by the fact that,
while in older colonies the young receive food from and are
cared for by a large number of workers, in incipient colonies the
young would be fed and tended only by the young parent adults,
whence their " nanitic " condition.   A dwarf-like condition
known as " nanism " also occurs among the ants.   These nanitic
individuals have not been provided with enough food in the
young stages.

The male and female termites are equally active in caring
for the young, and both young parent adults eat wood.   This
condition is quite strikingly in contrast to the lonely life of the
young queen of the " carpenter ant " (species of *Camponotus*) .
Here the consort male is dead and the queen without taking any

external nourishment has to feed and rear the first brood by her own efforts alone. Her food for a period of six months or more is obtained entirely from internal metabolic processes (or internal body changes), a breaking down of muscles, now useless, and of the reserve fat bodies into food.

The young termite parent adults are very busy with their housekeeping. Not only do they care for the eggs and young, carrying them in their mouths from place to place, but they also are cleanly. The small cell in which they live together is kept clean and the sides are smoothed; this is very simple! The cell and any débris are food; in eating they are also housecleaning. Later on, the king and queen will do nothing but add to the population. All care of young and of the nest will be done by the workers or nymphs.

Among the fungus-growing termites of the tropics there are " nurseries " or special chambers for the young, in addition to the permanent royal cell in a protected part of the mound nest. There are also "fungus gardens " where mushrooms are grown as a special food (fig. 24).

FIG. 24a. Fungus grown as food by a mound nesting termite in Java. *Photo. by Fairchild.*

While there are no nurseries in the nests of our native termites, the eggs are transported, and the young and older nymphs crawl or are carried, to warmer portions of the colony to secure more rapid development. In the spring they are to be found under wood or bark slabs on sunny hillsides where it is warmer than in the subterranean galleries.

Recently hatched young are fed on prepared, predigested food and do not eat wood until later in their development. The young are always active except during molting or short quiescent stages.

According to Dr. L. R. Cleveland, the young contain symbi-

otic intestinal protozoa twenty-four hours after hatching. This
clearly indicates that they are being fed on semi-liquid waste
products or excrement, or the so-called proctodeal food, by the
workers or nymphs, which is solicited from the anus. This substance apparently still contains food value. Even the older
termites have this habit and eagerly solicit such food by stroking
the posterior of the abdomen of workers or nymphs.

Analyses by the microchemical laboratory of the United States
Bureau of Chemistry show that lignin — a constituent of wood
— comprises the chief element in the excrement of subterranean
termites laid down as nest material; the termites cannot digest
lignin. This is in a very finely chewed or ground up condition.
The following are the results of analysis of a sample of the wood
which is the food of *Crypotermes brevis* Walker, the powder-post
termite, and the digested, excreted pellets:

	Wood used as food	Pellets of excreta
Moisture	7.59%	9.33%
Ash	.63%	3.43%
Ether Extract	2.11%	.26%
Protein	.35%	2.12%
Crude Fiber	63.40%	58.03%
Nitrogen Free Extract	25.92%	26.83%
	100.00%	100.00%

This analysis shows that in the main only cellulose has been
lost; and the remaining fiber is lignin, which cannot be digested.

Workers and soldiers develop to maturity in one year; no
nymphs of the sexual adults are produced during the first year.
Workers are quite evidently the caste most necessary in helping
to rear the new brood and enlarge the nest.

THE POST ADULT GROWTH

When the house fly changes into the winged adult, there is no
further growth in body size; if one sees smaller flies they are not
young but are different species. Among the termites, however,
in a young colony the abdomen of the adult queen has begun to
distend within a year after the swarm. Eventually, due to special diet and internal development, there will be an almost
unique, marked, " post adult " growth, and she becomes a physogastric queen.

With the increase in the number of egg tubes there is also an actual cellular division and growth, not a mere swelling up or distension. Even in the mature male or king there is a similar but comparatively slight post adult growth. Marked post adult growth also is to be seen in some of the insect guests found in nests of tropical termites.

The young pioneer termite female adults, or queens, have in the face of great difficulties established new colonies. With the post adult growth there is correlated degeneration of the jaw muscles. Now the queens, after rearing the first brood, become dependent upon the workers or young. No longer do they eat wood, but they are fed on a special prepared food received from the mouths of the workers. This is the same food from the mouth or " stomodeal " food given to the young and the soldiers. Much body color is also lost after the hidden underground or cryptobiotic life and since there is no longer any use for wings the thoracic muscles become degenerate.

Unless there are accidents all matings are for life, and second or third form kings and queens have been recorded as living together for as long as twenty-five years, at least in artificial colonies. Our native termites of course do not have as large physogastric queens as occur among tropical species. The age of queens can be estimated by watching the development of young colonies and measuring nest growth.

Old queens and kings lose portions of their feelers, legs, margins of the thorax, and some body cuticle. These parts are probably bitten off by workers or nymphs in their eagerness for exudate, which is licked from the body. Possibly parts might be lost through the workers' tugging at reproductive forms to guide them when changing position in the colony or changing the site of the colony.

In the case of tropical termites the size of the mound or carton nest and the number of pinnacles or chimneys on the mound nests aid in estimating the age of the queen. Old queens are somewhat shrunken and have the sides of the abdomen wrinkled. In old queens of the fungus-growing *Termes* (*Cyclotermes*) *obesus* Rambur of India, a dark blackish, longitudinal streak runs down the dorsum or back. This streak appears to follow the shape of the " wing muscles " of the heart. According to R. E. Snodgrass, this streak is not due to any degeneration of muscles or cells, but to sheets of dark brown nephrocytes in the cavity about the heart; the color is caused by the infiltration of dark granules. These nephrocytes are cells which secrete waste products and then migrate to the surface of the body to discharge.

HABITS OF THE REPRODUCTIVE ADULTS

The reproductive adults of our native termites are active and move about freely. No types of queens ever entirely lose their power of locomotion; there is no permanent " royal cell " as in many tropical species wherein the huge immobile queen is imprisoned. In consequence, the queens of our native termites are often difficult to find. Their location in the colony will depend upon the season of the year and the geographical locality of the species. The presence of runways of slightly larger diameter, to permit the passage of the mature egg-laying queens with distended abdomens, indicates that they are near-by in a cell.

In the more primitive " dry-wood " termites (species of *Kalotermes*) , the reproductive adults are often in the harder wood, such as knots, in the interior or more inaccessible portions of the wood. They cannot, as a rule, leave the wood, and are hence more restricted than are species of *Reticulitermes.* Queens of these lower or more primitive termites are relatively much smaller, have the abdomen less distended, and are more active than in the intermediate *Reticulitermes* or in the most highly specialized species of Termitidae, where they attain the largest size.

Among the species of *Reticulitermes,* the reproductive forms may be found either in the earth or in the wood. During warm summer weather, they migrate to cells above ground in the wood they are infesting; strange to relate they are often in the outer layers of wood, where they are afforded less protection but where there is greater warmth. In the winter in cold climates, they are below the frost line in the ground. Indeed, colonies readily migrate; they change the location of the nests to wood or soil, or shift the location within the wood according to the season or with temporary changes in the temperature and moisture conditions. The whole colony, even including the queen, may be moved to a new site if conditions become unfavorable.

In the prairie and in arid, desert regions, during periods of drought in summer, when the soil is hard baked and deeply cracked, the entire colony lives in deep subterranean galleries. The depth of the water table is the only factor which can limit the depth to which termites can penetrate into the soil.

Although their abdomens are also but slightly distended, the second form males are even more active than the first form males. They are usually present in a cell or cells with the queens, but on account of their smaller size they frequently escape when the colony is broken into. Sometimes when escape is shut off, males will attempt to hide under the greater bulk of the queen, but usually they desert their consorts at the first sign of danger.

Unlike the first form male adults, which are normally monogamous, second and third form adults are polygamous. A few males are associated with many females, usually in a series of cells in earth or wood; a ratio of four or more females of the second form to one male is not unusual. Seventeen females of the apterous or third form of *Reticulitermes flavipes* Kol. have been found in one colony in Virginia. In a colony of the Florida *Prorhinotermes* eight apterous females occurred with two males.

While smaller than the first form queens and having less egg-laying capacity, the greater number of these polygamous reproductive adults compensates, and their collective power of reproduction is greater.

In nature, in some colonies of the species of *Reticulitermes,* a single male adult of the first form may be found associated with numerous egg-laying females of the second form, in a ratio as great as sixteen to one. Probably these second form adults are utilized because of an accident to the single first form female. That is, occasionally there is interbreeding between the different types of reproductive adults within the species. Unfortunately, nothing is known of the resulting progeny.

In other colonies, egg-laying second and third form females have on rare occasions been found associated together in a small colony; it is regretted that no associated males have been found.

No doubt in nature, when one or both parent reproductive forms have been lost, young reproductive forms present in the colony as nymphs are utilized in replacement. Furthermore, the development of these nymphs in an emergency doubtless may be hastened by special care and feeding by the workers.

Studies are being carried on in breeding and cross-breeding

these different reproductive adults of termites within the species, to determine the progeny of the castes and the explanation of the origin of the castes. Only a beginning has been made, owing to the comparatively long time it takes termites to complete their development, as well as to difficulties in technique, which have led to the dying out of artificial colonies or the killing of them by moulds or externally parasitic mites or by internally parasitic nematodes.

It may eventually be proven that new species of *Reticulitermes* are being evolved, i.e., there are now " nascent " species, or species in the making. Certain species are very close morphologically, and races or sub-species exist with composite characters; close species may be merely variations! Or, since termites are plastic, or easily moulded, it may be that there is a tendency toward a mean, and in reality there are no sub-species. Here is an excellent opportunity to learn whether there is cross-breeding between species and the consequent production of hybrids; whether interbreeding between the different reproductive types within the species — which occurs in nature, but which we have not been able to promote artificially in glass breeding cages — may result in progeny differing from the normal. Dr. L. R. Cleveland in 1924 succeeded in obtaining eggs from the crossing of first form, or macropterous, female adults and second form, or brachypterous, male adults, but was not able to rear these — only, it is believed, because conditions in the cages were not favorable.

In an attempt to determine the progeny of such crosses, during the early spring of 1931 large scale breeding and crossing experiments were again instituted at Washington, D. C., with reproductive forms of the termite *Reticulitermes flavipes* Kol. There have been differences in the results of breeding experiments carried on by entomologists in this country and abroad. In the case of species of *Reticulitermes,* my earlier experiments have shown that the first brood reared by first form, macropterous adults are all nanitic or dwarf workers except one or two soldiers. The first brood of second form or brachypterous adults appear to be the same; but even in long-established colonies no first form adults are produced where the parents are second form. Of course where the parent adults are first form, winged or first form adults are later produced. No success, so far, has been attained in breeding third form, or apterous, reproductive adults in these artificial colonies maintained in the laboratory.

Like the normal first form adults, complementary or substitute second and third forms are true adult castes. They apparently breed true to type over long periods and never produce first form adults. Imms and the late Dr. Thompson have accepted the view which I myself hold, that the origin of the termite castes can best be explained by genetics: there is a parallelism between these castes and Mendelian segregants, or individuals with a dissociation of characters in the formation of germs. While the progeny would vary with the age of the colony of termites and with the genus or at least with the family, the character of the brood might be predicted by generalized formulae.

Crossing was tried both with single pairs of males and females and with large numbers of males and females or gregarious colonies, i.e., an association of several colonies. The pure colonies of males and females of the same type produced the same results obtained previously. The crosses between first form and second form adults were in aggregate colonies of large numbers of females to small numbers of males (as many as seventeen to thirty-four), and workers and soldiers were also present.

Sexual attraction was immediately evidenced in the crossed as well as in the pure colonies. Apparently there was no difference in degree: whether the male was first or second form, the female of the opposite type was equally attractive and attracted, for this caudal attraction of male to female was also to be observed in attraction of the female to the male.

To date, these experiments in genetics conducted during 1931 confirm the results of previous breedings first begun in 1911. The progeny of pure colonies of first form males and females is the same during the first nine months whether the colonies are in the aggregate or whether a single male and female produce the brood.

Gregarious colonies, or an association of several colonies, appear to be relatively somewhat healthier and more aggressive than those where the parents consist of a single male and female. This is interesting in connection with the experiments of Dr. W. C. Allee of the University of Chicago relating to the rôle of aggregation in ecology. These experiments tend to show that groups of animals of the same kind react to each other or their surroundings in a somewhat different manner than do individuals. Aggregations may be beneficial or adverse to the individuals involved.

Of course our data, in the case of termites, are meager and inconclusive. The termites' practice of cleaning mould or mycelium off each other during " trophallaxis " or exchange of body secretions or exudates by licking each other might explain these more favorable conditions in gregarious colonies.

The ten colonies of the crosses established on April 29 and 30 were in healthy condition on May 11; the males and females were active in cells together and the second form reproductive adults with short wing pads were attaining a deeper yellow-brown pigmentation. On May 15 about three dozen eggs were present in one colony. Nematodes, or round worms, were abundant in some of the colonies and apparently destroyed two colonies. On May 17 the eggs were being tended by workers. On May 29 the workers were moving the eggs about from place to place so that sometimes the eggs were visible, at other times not. All but two of the surviving colonies had now died, probably due to infection with mould. On June 1, the eggs were fewer in number.

On June 25 young termites several days old were observed in the colony where the seven males were second form or brachypterous, and the sixteen females were first form, or macropterous. On June 17, 24, and 29 a few young termites of different ages were observed in both remaining colonies; at least five young were visible at one time.

On July 3 no young or first form adults were observed, all being dead, and the complementary second form male adults were eating the workers alive, a piece at a time, workers being observed in various stages of dismemberment and the males actually feeding on them. On July 30 this colony was nearly all dead. On August 8 the second form males were still alive and on September 1 several second form males and a few workers survived.

On September 4, three first form females were added to this colony from replacement colonies to continue the experiment. On September 12 both the males and females were alive but most of the workers had been eaten alive in spite of the fact that food and moisture conditions appeared to be satisfactory. On

October 2 the first form females were dead but had not been eaten; all the workers had disappeared. On October 22 only one or two moribund second form males were alive, in a very weakened and shrunken condition.

On July 18, in the gregarious colony where the first form males were outnumbered by the second form females in the ratio 22 to 11, newly hatched young were observed. On July 30 this colony was nearly all dead and no young remained.

These experiments confirm observations in nature which prove that the various reproductive adults do cross-breed within the species and that they will do so in artificial colonies. In previous experiments only eggs had been obtained from similar crossings. It is hoped that this intensely interesting and important work in breeding and crossing can be repeated. Large numbers of colonies are necessary and the experiment takes considerable time and patience but is well worth while.

We still are unable to tell what is the progeny of these crosses, but the author believes that the character of the progeny can be predicted by genetic formulae. Biologists are groping for truth and searching for natural laws, as was the brilliant poet William Blake in his *The Tiger*. We may well ask — What immortal hand?

CHAPTER IV

NESTS

TERMITES were architects long before the advent of man on earth. In the tropics their hard, earth-like carton or mound nests are built in trees (as with arboreal man), or in excavations below ground (as the cave man), or as low, hut-like mounds or lofty skyscrapers on and above the ground (as present man) (fig. 25). Termites have not only constructed primitive rammed earth or Pieazo and "'dobe" houses but well-ventilated and rain-shedding pagodas, which would be worthy of modern ventilation engineering and air conditioning. Natives of the Transvaal, South Africa, according to Claude Fuller, have venerated certain termite mounds for many hundreds of years; the mounds have remained unchanged through the ages.

The 1978 species of termites of the entire world can be classified or grouped into three types, namely: non-subterranean or dry-wood termites, including rotten wood and powder-post termites, which do not burrow in the ground but attack the wood of buildings or trees directly; subterranean or soil-nesting termites which attack the wood of buildings, trees, or living crops indirectly from burrows in the earth; and mound and carton tree nest building termites, which are also subterranean in habit — these do not occur in continental United States. Here, we have only two types to consider.

These types enable one to discuss termites intelligently, without using a series of long Latin names, which, of course, would vary with the extremely diverse species or geographical locality. Although the termites of the world have widely different habits and habitats, these groups also serve as a basis for control operations. That is, the control measures for any one type of termite, with possibly slight modifications, will be the same for any region in the world.

In the lower and intermediate termites, as a rule, the nests are diffused and more or less temporary. Colonies in these nests are more or less subject to migration when conditions become unfavorable. Among the higher termites, especially in the tropics, nests are concentrated and more permanent.

FIG. 25. A. Hard mound nests of the termite *Amitermes medius* Bks. in the savannah region of Panama. It is difficult to break into these nests with a pickaxe.
B. Carton tree nest of a nasutiform termite.

From the viewpoint of the ecologist or student of life in relation to other life or its surroundings, the species with conspicuous concentrated nests will yield the richest harvest in colony life; that is, in the mound nests on the ground, or in the carton nests on the ground or on trees will be found the greatest diversity of life, both of the termites and of their various associates. The systematist or classifier finds, however, that collecting

in wood where colonies are nonconspicuous or diffused at present yields the most new forms.

None of the 56 termites which occur in continental United States construct the conspicuous mound nests — such striking features of certain portions of the tropics. Nor do they live in carton nests on tree trunks or on the ground. Our native termites also do not have particularly striking habits, as compared for instance with the foraging or harvesting wander termites of Africa, South America, or the Orient, which come out into full sunlight and march about in long files. Nearctic or North American termites do not culti-

FIG. 25a. Nest of *Nasutitermes* (*Lacessitermes*) *batavus* Kemner on stump in Chinchona plantation, Totasari, Java, December, 1895. *Photo. by David Fairchild.*

vate fungi for food. Nevertheless, the termites of the United States do have interesting habits and are as worthy of close study as the tropical species.

It is believed that the biology of our common subterranean species of *Reticulitermes* presents many complexities possibly not to be found or not yet discovered among other termites. Not realizing such differences, popular literature often attributes habits to our native termites only possessed by tropical species. One cannot thus generalize, even when dealing with the species of only one continent. Our termites when carefully studied do not need to have their habits of living " dressed up ". This is just as flagrant an error as are the references to the nightingale as a native bird in American poetry of the colonial period.

The nests of North American termites are hidden within wood or below ground, and consequently termites are seldom seen except at the time of the swarm.

The "rotten wood" termites, species of *Zoötermopsis* (see

Table II, under Addenda), confined to the Pacific Coast, Montana, Nevada, Arizona, and New Mexico, and the "powder-post" termites are merely subdivisions of the "dry-wood" group of termites, which are distributed throughout the warmer regions of the world. These termites and the Florida *Prorhinotermes* do not burrow into the earth; hence they are non-subterranean in habit. Certain primitive species such as those in *Zoötermopsis* and *Archotermopsis* may inhabit ice and snow covered logs and stumps in colder temperate regions.

Flying to and attacking wood directly (fig. 26), they have no permanent nest; and colonies are diffused through the wood of dead trees, logs, stumps, and branches, or in scars or dead areas in the trunks, roots, or branches of living trees. Instead of following the grain of the wood continuously, they cut across and excavate through it longitudinal chambers of limited length connected by

FIG. 26. Entrance holes of dry-wood termites burrowed directly into wood. These holes are about the size of a BB shot.

tunnels. The first form sexual adults, after they have lost their wings, and the young or nymphs are the destructive forms. Their pellets of partly digested excreted wood are regularly impressed (fig. 27), and sometimes completely fill or block up the burrows in a compact mass; they are often expelled as dry droppings from the infested wood and serve as a warning of infestation.

Neither the dry-wood nor the powder-post termites require much moisture. They can exist without the great amount of moisture necessary to the life of termites which are subterranean in habit, and can live in wood containing less than the 12–15% of moisture normally contained in air-dried wood. They are never ground-nesting, and only rarely do a few species leave the

wood and burrow in the earth. In the United States these termites are confined to a narrow belt along the southern seacoast
(fig. 28) .

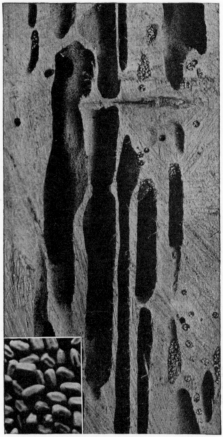

Fig. 27. Pellets of excrement in burrows in
rafter in " adobe " building in Arizona
burrowed by dry-wood termites; note the
chambers running across the grain of the
wood.
Inset: Impressed pellets of fine, digested,
excreted wood expelled from infested wood
by dry-wood termites; these pellets serve
as a warning of infestation. Enlarged.

Colonies also may be found in fence posts, in telephone and
other poles, in derricks, and in the woodwork and furniture in

buildings. Rarely in continental United States does this type
of termite damage living trees. Such cases of injury to the roots
and trunks of living citrus trees are caused by species of *Neotermes* or dry-wood termites in California and Florida. In the
tropics, such injury causes losses to teak, tea, rubber, and other
trees. It has only recently been discovered that these termites,
species of *Neotermes,* which prefer a more damp wood than the
other, more normal "dry-wood" termites, can burrow in the
ground and infest trees through their roots and are somewhat
of a moist wood type.

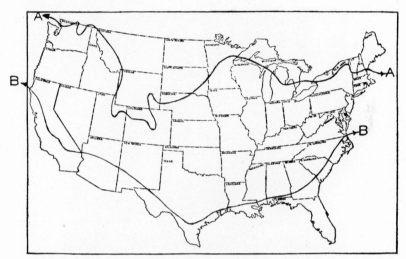

FIG. 28. Map showing (line A–A) the northern limit of damage done by
subterranean termites in the United States and (line B–B) the northern
limit of damage done by dry-wood or non-subterranean termites, as of
June 1935.

The "powder-post" groups are able to live in very dry, seasoned wood and are actual or potential "house termites". They
are injurious to the woodwork and furniture, etc., and may be
carried abroad in furniture, wooden trunks, picture frames, etc.
Species may thus become cosmopolitan in so far as conditions
of climate are suitable. So far, species brought into the United
States in furniture have not become established. Often damage
is more apparent than real, but sometimes only a thin exterior
shell is left on hollowed-out wood; holes are plugged up with
excrement (fig. 29).

Subterranean termites are much more widespread and common in continental United States (fig. 28) than are the non-subterranean species. These termites nest in the ground, or excavate galleries in wood near, on, or in the earth. Tropical termites have concentrated nests, but our native termite nests are diffused and galleries often cover wide areas of ground. Unlike the dry-wood termites, they attack wood indirectly from or through the ground. They can migrate from the wood, which is a very unusual occurrence among the dry-wood group.

Destructive wood-borers, the subterranean type can penetrate

FIG. 29.   Holes in infested wood sealed up by a native "powder-post" termite (*Cryptotermes brevis* Walk.), utilizing excrement.

the hardest of woods, but like all termites are selective feeders and borers, following the line of least resistance. In addition to galleries in wood, they excavate a labyrinth of underground passages in the soil, usually under or near wood or vegetation.

They are essentially ground-nesting in habit and must maintain a connection with the earth — which is the source of the moisture so necessary to their life. There is no permanent true nest, as a rule, except in subterranean species in the tropics. The colonies are more or less scattered or diffused throughout the wood of dead trees, stumps, logs, scars on the trunks of living trees, branches, etc.

These termites fill all holes or large cavities in wood with earth and excreted wood, which mastic wood filler keeps out insect enemies, conserves humidity and adds strength to the structure: the whole has a conglomerate appearance, due to the irregular deposits of excreted finely digested wood (fig. 30).

Colonies in fence posts, telephone and other poles, towers, derricks, mine props, and the foundations, woodwork, and contents of buildings cause subterranean termites to be classed as very injurious insects.

In the case of timber and woodwork of buildings, subterranean termites are responsible for 95% of all damage caused by

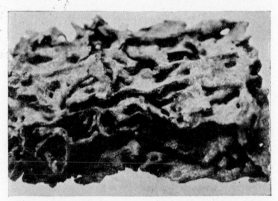

Fig. 30. Excrement mixed with earth used by native subterranean termites in filling cavities; after drying it becomes very hard.

termites throughout the world, while only 5% of such damage can be charged to the non-subterranean type.

In continental United States termite damage to living trees, shrubs, crops, flowers, and other vegetation, while occasionally occurring and being temporarily a very local problem, in general is not serious. However, in the tropics damage to valuable trees and to living crops by termites is of considerable economic importance.

The galleries of subterranean termites follow the grain of the wood, which they honeycomb by eating away the larger celled, faster growing tissue, leaving the smaller celled, denser wood untouched (fig. 31). They secretly, silently, and ceaselessly eat away the wood which shelters them, and often cause serious damage before their presence is detected. A thin outer shell of wood is always left on wood, and termites seldom so

Fig. 31. *Above:* Heavy structural timbers damaged by native subterranean termites; note how they followed the grain of the wood.
Below: Damage to expensive oak flooring by the common subterranean termite. Note that damage is not apparent on upper surface; often such damage is not detected until a chair or table leg accidentally breaks through the outer layer of uneaten wood.

entirely consume the wood fibers of timber that all structural strength is gone and it collapses. This would leave them

exposed to enemies, and to lack of moisture and consequent
desiccation.

Periodically inundated regions are unfavorable for subterranean termites, but like the non-subterranean group they are
occasionally found in driftwood. Cold and warm climates, arid
regions or deserts and swampy areas are alike inhabited by these

FIG. 32. *Above:* Carton, earth-like shelter tubes constructed by a subterranean termite over brick wall in dark, heated, damp basement; these
tubes are used in passing over impenetrable substances. Also view of
similar tube over concrete wall.
Below: Enlarged view of tubes to show their texture.

termites. The nests of our subterranean termites (species of
Reticulitermes) are not permanent — as are the mound nests
in the tropics. These species have wandering habits and there
are seasonal changes in colony life.

The center of activity in termite colonies changes with the
seasons, due to varying needs as to conditions of warmth and
moisture. In the eastern United States, in spring, when there

is abundant moisture, outlying galleries of colonies are teeming
with life, where, during the heat of summer, conditions would
be too dry.   In arid regions termites burrow deep into the
ground; consequently in summer they bury themselves more
deeply, going into the less exposed galleries.   In the late autumn
or at the beginning of winter (in northern Virginia, late October or early November) they enter the ground and do not
come above ground till late in February or early in March.

Fig. 33.   Shelter tubes of our common eastern subterranean termite leading from a door frame towards the floor above.

Again, the colony readily migrates and the site is abandoned if
conditions become unfavorable.   A single colony may be spread
over an extensive area, and it is often impossible to define the
limits of a colony.   At higher altitudes in the Appalachian
Mountains, in the canyons of the Southwest, and in high
mountains in the West, termite colonies in the earth and under
stones are more common.

In the desert regions in the United States, termites (*Reticuli-*

termes) are to be found between the leaf rosettes at the bases of agave; in yucca, Joshua tree and agave stems; and in cacti, as are also species of *Kalotermes*. In prairie regions in the roots and stems of sage brush are found species of subterranean termites (*Reticulitermes*) or elsewhere where there is moisture. Species in the family Termitidae are to be found in similar locations in desert regions.

Metal, stone, brick, concrete, and other substances which

Fig. 34. Hanging shelter tubes made from wood to earth by native subterranean termites.

these termites cannot penetrate are bridged over by means of granular, earth-like shelter tubes, which are, as a rule, of small diameter (fig. 32), although these tubes, especially in clay soil, may sometimes be thick or wide. Such tubes occasionally are suspended from beams or are constructed upright from the earth or the floor of a building (figs. 35 and 36). In the latter case the tubes are heavily buttressed at the base, like a southern or bald cypress tree. Usually, however, they run over some surface, such as a wall or a tree trunk; and they are often extended up to great heights on trees in tropical countries. Great depths too can be penetrated by termites, the water table being the only limit.

These carton tubes or " 'dobe " subways enable termites to carry earth, their source of protection and moisture, with them above ground, over stones, high up tree trunks, or elsewhere. In the sand of the desert, tubes built down into the sand keep the termites from being exposed by the wind blowing away the sand.

In continental United States there are no mound or carton nest building species of highly specialized termites. The re-

Fig. 35. Suspended shelter tubes built by termites from infested timbers down to the soil underneath a building.

lated species, native to this country, are all of subterranean habit; very few of these higher or specialized termites are destructive wood borers.

In southwestern United States the " desert termites " (species of *Gnathamitermes*), which nest deep in the soil, cover over vegetation with earth-like tubes (fig. 38), usually working at night after rains. In pasture land such earth-like coverings kill the green forage plants, often over large areas. This injurious habit is beneficial to the termites since the vegetation either becomes chemically altered by fungi or contains fungi which directly serve as food for the termites. The exact relationship between these termites and fungi has not been thoroughly studied,

as yet. These termites do not contain intestinal protozoa to
break down the cellulose into available food, and hence fungi
either are important in their diet or alter the form of the vegetation to make it available as food. Buckley first described the
habits of a similar protozoa-less, nasutiform termite in 1860.
" It was about sunset on October 22, 1860, when I first saw
this species in a field, where both workers and nasuti were
carrying home seeds of grasses and weeds. They marched in

Fig. 36. Buttressed shelter tubes built up
free from the ground.

dense columns along pathways leading to a hole near the base
of a stump, into which they entered. . . . They dwell in the
ground where they have rooms, seldom more than one to two
inches long, connected by tunnels. . . . After rains — which
are of rare occurrence in that climate — they make semi-cylin-
drical tubes, which lie on the ground with a length of from three
to six inches. These arched ways sometimes intercept each
other, being connected with chambers; but they rarely work by
day above the surface and never in bright sunshine."

While popular opinion of termites is that they are essentially a moisture-loving group of insects, this is only partially true, at least with regard to habitats. Subterranean termites require much moisture, but the dry-wood termites are able to live in wood containing a minimum of natural or inherent moisture. When in 1929, with members of the Termite Investigations Committee of the University of California, I was about to leave on a collecting trip into the Mojave and Colorado deserts of California, I met a friend. Knowing that my " hunting " was confined almost entirely to termites, he was astounded. " Surely

FIG. 37. Free shelter tubes built up from infested wood; note how the tubes are interlaced. Photographs by Dr. Hermann von-Schrenk.

you don't expect to find termites in the arid deserts," was his comment on the trip.

Termites do occur in deserts: they thrive in the roots and trunks of Joshua trees, cacti, Spanish bayonets, agave, etc. These insects have been found in the Sahara and Kalahari deserts in Africa. As has been shown, they are found in sage brush roots and stems in treeless arid areas of far western United States and in dry plains and prairies of our southwestern states. Termites can adapt themselves and in one way or another obtain the necessary moisture where none appears to exist.

There are no " mixed " colonies among termites in the sense in which they occur among ants. Termites do not raid other termite nests and do not make slaves of captives. Some termites are " social parasites " in the sense that they live in a portion of a nest made by another species; the galleries are separate, however, and the species do not intermingle.

Fig. 38. Earth-like shelter tubes of a desert termite covering low vegetation in Texas.

In some nests, especially in carton and mound nests of tropical termites, first form or macropterous queens in numbers ranging from two to sixteen may occur in the same nest. This may be explained either as polygamy or as aggregation — i.e., many pairs of young males and females helped to build a single nest. The latter sometimes occurs in the case of our native species of subterranean termites (*Reticulitermes*). Several colonies may be started under the moist bark of a decaying log and later the surviving members of the separate colonies become more or less merged.

CHAPTER V

THE FOOD OF TERMITES

ONLY recently have investigations been made of the exact feeding habits of wood-boring insects. In the cases where such studies have been conducted, it has been demonstrated, as a rule, that wood-feeding insects do not directly digest wood. Wood, or its chief constituent, cellulose, serves termites as shelter for their nests as well as food. This is not the case among the wood-boring " carpenter ants " such as species *Camponotus* and *Crematogaster* which merely utilize wood as shelter and do not eat it. It is among the sub-social wood-boring insects, especially the beetles, that life is longest, and here there is an association of the two sexes for rearing the young. Wood diet is broken down into available form in various different manners among such insects: fungi and protozoa have lately been found to play important rôles. Among the primitive, subsocial roaches, the same association between parents and young occurs, and wood also serves as diet. But in these roaches, as in certain termites, protozoa are present in their intestines in a symbiotic relationship and wood which they ingest is made available as food for their host termites by the action of enzymes.

This food of termites, cellulose, can be obtained from both living and dead vegetation; termites are among the few forest insects that attack both living and dead forest trees. In the United States, however, termites constitute no problem in the forest. In the intestines of most termites is a living fauna and flora of great diversity present in enormous numbers. Various types of microscopic protozoa, flagellates or forms with whip-like appendages, amoebae, spirochaetes, and fungi occur. Some of these protozoa contain enzymes which digest the cellulose of wood for the termites; without the protozoa the termites cannot live (fig. 39).

Although suspected for a long time, only about ten years ago was this indirect digestion of wood by termites definitely proven by a young student from Tennessee at the Johns Hopkins University in Baltimore, Maryland — Dr. L. R. Cleveland. By removing the essential intestinal protozoa, he was able to prove that without these symbiants termites could not live on a cellulose diet. The protozoa were removed at first by heat and later by oxygenation. If the protozoa from these termites whose intestines had been " defaunated " were replaced, then they could live.

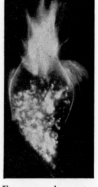

Of course, the protozoa could be replaced by allowing other normal termites to feed them partly digested wood. When fed on broken down or partly digested cellulose, such as is found in dry cow droppings or " chips," they could likewise survive.

When I said essential protozoa, I meant that only a certain proportion of these intestinal protozoa appear to be of importance in this helpful symbiotic rôle. The many thousands of protozoa that occur as a seething mass in the intestines of termites are of different kinds or species. Several different species may occur in each host species of termite.

Fig. 39. A protozoan found in the intestines of termites; these are necessary to the life of the termites since they contain enzymes which digest cellulose, the principal food of these termites. Greatly magnified.

Termites are the nucleus of a complex association of plant and animal life, especially in the tropics where they live in large permanent nests. Other species than the host termite may be present: various other animal or plant associates occur in different rôles, and there are, of course, the varied intestinal fauna and flora.

As has been stated, the rôle of some of the more primitive and minute organisms found associated with termites is not known. Spirochaetes, intermediate between plants and animals, occur in the intestines of termites, but it is not known what their relation is to termites. Dr. L. R. Cleveland has recently discovered that they do not benefit the host termites or aid in digestion, as do the protozoan amoebae and flagellates, which contain the enzymes that digest cellulose (the basis of the structure of all plants) .

Aside from the interesting study of the protozoa themselves, such comparative study may help to differentiate between closely related species of termites, and in certain groups of termites may make possible specific determination from immature or fragmentary termite material, especially desirable when specimens of termites need be cut from valuable furniture with as little damage to the latter as possible. Such studies should aid in plotting geographical distribution and relationships. Indeed, there is some evidence after preliminary studies of these protozoa by Dr. H. Kirby, Jr., of the University of California, that there may be a correlation between the evolution or development through geological time (phylogeny) of the host termites and their intestinal protozoa. The question of the transfer of the protozoa between termites is important, as is the possibility of the transfer of protozoa between primitive, wood-boring roaches and termites.

These soft-bodied termites, whose bodies are full of juices, must have a wonderful chemical laboratory in their bodies, or they could not live in very dry wood, as do the *Cryptotermes* group, or " powder-post " termites, or without the element nitrogen. It must be that either directly, or indirectly through their intestinal plant and animal parasites, they manufacture metabolic water from the air and cellulose, as well as fix atmospheric nitrogen into forms available to them as food — for animals must have nitrogen in order to live. Probably fungi provide the water and nitrogen. Termites cannot obtain nitrogen from their normal food, which is derived entirely from vegetation.

The rôle of bacteria and fungi in the intestines of termites is still obscure. It is possible that nitrogen is obtained from the fungi either directly or indirectly through their bodies, by their breaking down cellulose. There is a complex symbiotic association of plant and animal life in the intestines of many termites not fully understood at the present time.

It is interesting to speculate as to whether primitive termites obtained their intestinal protozoa from the older primitive wood-boring roaches, which contain similar protozoa, and as to whether it is possible that the higher, more specialized termites, which have but few intestinal protozoa, obtained these by transfer from the lower termites. Often many different kinds of termites live closely associated in wood, in the earth, or in nests.

Much further study will be necessary before these problems can be solved, if they ever can be solved!

Not all termites, however, have these helpful protozoa in their intestines. The higher, more specialized termites (*Termes*-group), those which build mound nests in Africa and the Orient, cultivate mushrooms for food in special fungus gardens, and so obtain their cellulose indirectly; it is digested for them by these low forms of plant life, which obtain the cellulose from vegetation.

Since wood is the commonest source of cellulose, naturally it is the food of most termites. Some specialized nasutiform termites in the Oriental region that do not feed on wood or cultivated fungi forage in columns in search of lichens for food. In Africa and South America other foraging or harvesting termites proceed in files in the open during the day to collect grass stems or other vegetation. Low forms of plant life break down the contained cellulose into available food after it is stored in the warm, moist underground nests.

All of these daylight foraging termites, although ranging from primitive to highly specialized forms, are dark-colored and have well-developed eyes.

In North America, including the southwestern United States, there are a few species of nasutiform termites which forage in dense columns for vegetation, usually after sunset. Birds, lizards, and toads eat many of them.

Still other termites are to be found in the southwestern portions of the United States, living deep in the ground under dry " cow chips " or droppings. In meadows and pasture land are nests of these termite species of *Gnathamitermes* and *Anoplotermes,* or the " soldier-less " termites.

Cow chips or excreta are practically a predigested or broken-down food, and no intestinal protozoa which aid in the digestion of the cellulose of wood occur in these termites. Kirby states that a small amoeba not occurring in any recent Kalotermitid is present in *Gnathamitermes* or the desert termites.

Species of our native desert termites or *Gnathamitermes* have already been described as covering living vegetation with moist earth, thus causing at least a partial breaking-down of the cellulose.

This same principle is used by man in accelerated laboratory tests of the durability or decay resistance of untreated or treated woods. " Fungus pits " are constructed in technical laboratories where wood can be kept warm and moist, thus greatly hastening the growth of wood-destroying fungi.

Species of *Gnathamitermes* do not contain the usual symbiotic intestinal protozoa, but either fungi alter the vegetation so as to make it available to them as food, or the fungi themselves are important in the diet of the termites. These termites will also

FIG. 40. Nodules found in the nest of a nasutiform termite. These are a possible reserve food supply.

cover wood with similar earth mats and eat off or scour the surface, but never bore into or destroy wood.

Certain tropical mandibulate and nasutiform termites which build " carton " nests in trees store what is thought by some to be food in large solid lumps or nodules. These small potato-like spheres consist of excreted wood and are supposed to be a reserve food supply (fig. 40). Excreta often pass through the bodies of several termites before finally being rejected as without further food value.

CANNIBALISM. Termites sometimes vary their strictly vegeta-

tion or cellulose diet to one of raw meat, by eating their own
eggs, young, or colony mates.   Like some ants, the parent or
parents in incipient termite colonies eat some eggs and newly
hatched young.   Unlike the solitary queen carpenter ant mother
(*Camponotus* species) of a young colony, who takes no nourishment until eggs are laid, the young termite king and queen eat
wood while rearing the first brood of young.   Eggs and young
appear to be less likely to be eaten in colonies headed by first
form parents than in colonies headed by second form adults or
in colonies where there are crosses between these two reproductive forms.

True cannibalism is more often observed in artificial colonies
maintained in the laboratory, where healthy young and workers
are eaten alive, a piece at a time, although food and moisture
conditions are apparently favorable.   Cannibalism gives an easy
and quick access to rich concentrated food and moisture.   It
probably is a more common occurrence, even under more natural conditions in the life of the termite colony, than has been
generally supposed.   As a rule, sickly individuals and those having difficulty in molting have been more commonly observed
to be eaten in colonies in nature.

Indeed, cannibalism, especially among the young, of many
different kinds of insects is much more frequent than has been
recorded.

Young termites, as well as soldiers and post-adult queens, are
unable to feed themselves, due to various different causes.
Hence, they are fed, from the mouths of the workers, predigested
cellulose.   This regurgitated food is only one type of special
food.   Another source of such food is the anus, from which a
semi-liquid substance is solicited by stroking the end of the abdomen with the feelers or antennae.   These foods are termed
"stomodeal" and "proctodeal" to indicate their origin.

During the process of grooming each other to obtain exudate,
rotten wood termites often stroke the abdomen of other termites
and obtain semi-liquid material from the anus.   A termite eating such food will sometimes be accosted by one or several others
who attempt to steal the morsel.   The termite which solicited
the food originally will retreat and be pursued in a manner sug-
gesting the habit of birds about a bread crumb.

The young or nymphs contain intestinal protozoa twenty-four hours after hatching, which shows that they are being fed by the parents, workers, or older nymphs (from the ani) and are not yet eating wood. This ingestion of protozoa soon enables them to eat wood themselves.

ANTHROPOCENTRISM. It is not scientific to attribute human traits to insects. It is very conceited for man to consider himself the center of the universe in all matters   Human beings reason, but the actions of insects are instinctive. whether undertaken for the individual or for the colony. We must not confuse morals with behavior. To say that insects see, smell, taste, feel, and hear in the same sense that man does is being anthropocentric.

Among termites selfishness is the basis of life and progress. Despite this, their colony life has always excited interest in man. The care of the brood and queen by the workers, and the alarm manifested by worker and soldier termites when the colony is broken into and the brood or queen disturbed, have called forth praise. In these prosaic days of biological facts, much of the mystery of the complex social system of the termites which leads to admiration by man has had to go by the board. Many fantastic theories have collapsed.

TROPHALLAXIS. Dr. W. M. Wheeler's theory of "trophallaxis" or exchange of nourishment can explain many of the actions on the basis of which the parental feelings of man have been attributed to insects. Termites constantly groom or lick the surfaces of each other's bodies to obtain secretions or "exudate," which they eagerly solicit. The procedure is to stroke the body with the antennae, then groom the body with the mouth, or solicit directly from the mouth or anus of another termite. Exudate is obtained even from the surface of the eggs. Hence, many actions and reactions of termites may be explained by this eagerness for exudate or a desire for the special forms of nourishment obtained by grooming or solicited from another termite or colony guest. The cooperative relationship between adult termites and their young is, while probably purely selfish, adequate.

During the exchange of food, termites assiduously groom each other by licking; and this habit, as will be shown later, can be taken advantage of in poisoning certain termites in economic control work.

Termites are " selective " feeders, and also, as a rule, follow the lines of least resistance in boring through material which they cannot or do not eat. Physical characteristics of wood such as hardness do not deter termite attack, since even lignum-vitae (*Guaiacum sanctum*), a very hard, heavy, or dense tropical wood, is eaten by termites in Haiti and in Middle America.

METHODS AND TESTS. Various tests have been conducted by the federal Bureau of Entomology to determine what chemical extractives or principles native to certain woods cause them to be resistant to termites. Tests have also been carried on for many years to discover what chemical wood preservatives are the most effective in deterring termite attack and what are the best methods of impregnating timber with chemicals.

Tests of chemical wood preservatives, of methods of super-ficial treatment and of treatment by impregnation, and of natu-rally termite resistant woods have been conducted by the Bureau of Entomology, in cooperation with the Forest Products Labora-tory in the United States, since 1911, when several series of ground or "graveyard" tests were instituted at Falls Church, Virginia. The soil of the test area was rather heavily infested with several subterranean termites (species of *Reticulitermes*), since woodland was nearby and wooden fences surrounding the test area were rather heavily infested.

From time to time, additional termites were artificially placed in these areas by laying heavily infested logs on the ground and removing them during the winter when the termites had left the wood and gone into the soil below the frost line. It is felt that some reliable data have been obtained from these rather small scale tests, but, due to the fact that there was practically no termite activity from October until March, it was believed that supplementary tests should be made in the tropics, where much quicker results could be obtained under more favorable conditions. Consequently, in 1924, tests were begun on Barro Colorado Island, Canal Zone, Panama (frontispiece). My friends began to say, " Snyder starts graveyard tests everywhere that he goes."

Dr. F. M. Chapman, famous authority on birds of the Ameri-can Museum of Natural History, in 1929 described this island in his book, *My Tropical Air Castle*. The Institute for Research in Tropical America, established by the National Research

PLATE II. Model or demonstration termite-proof building constructed entirely of timber impregnated with standard chemical wood preservatives, located in a tropical jungle on Barro Colorado Island, Canal Zone, Panama. The timber and finish in this building were impregnated with the preservatives most suitable for their position in the building. Many species of wood-destroying termites occur on this Island. The building was completed in October, 1926 and is undamaged in 1935.

Council, has sponsored the establishment of the Barro Colorado Island Laboratory in the Canal Zone, as a government wild life reservation and research station. One's first visit to this naturalist's paradise, in Gatun Lake midway between the Atlantic and Pacific Coasts, gives one the impression of being in an entirely new and different world. Towering, vine-covered, huge trees, often with gaudy blossoms, luxuriant vegetation, ferns and other tropical fauna on these trees and on the ground, grotesque birds of brilliant plumage and weird note, strange animals and insects transport one. At daybreak noisy parrots and howling monkeys amaze one. At dusk large cicadas herald with loud crescendos the coming darkness or the cooling of the atmosphere. It is an unforgettable experience.

In the dense, hot, humid jungle, many wood-destroying termites exist. With Mr. James Zetek, in charge of this laboratory, I have conducted many and varied tests of native and exotic timbers. The relative resistance of these timbers to termites is being determined in these long-time tests, as well as what grade or grades — usually the denser, closer grained heartwood — are most resistant. Chemical extractives, natural to certain woods, render them distasteful to termites.

These experiments are, of course, being made so that the results can be available for commercial purposes. Hence, they are conducted as service tests on a large scale. In addition to tests of timbers and sections of telegraph poles, inhabitable buildings, bridges, watch towers and water tanks have been specially built for purposes of experiment (frontispiece).

Furniture, both treated and untreated, and various types of wood pulp and fiber wall and insulation board are included in the Panama tests, as part of the buildings; such composition boards can be poisoned during the process of manufacture so as to render them resistant to termite attack.

As a further supplement to these tests in Virginia and Panama, in 1928 an International Termite Exposure Test was instituted by the Bureau of Entomology and the Forest Products Laboratory in cooperation with the governments of South Africa, Australia, Hawaii and Panama, to test similarly treated woods. In addition to obtaining results under widely different environmental conditions, it is hoped to eliminate any possibility of personal bias. Reports on the results of these experiments are

PLATE III. Building constructed on Barro Colorado Island, Canal Zone, Panama, of close-grained heartwood redwood (*Sequoia sempervirens*) from the Pacific Coast of the United States to test the resistance of this special grade of redwood to attack by both subterranean and dry-wood termites. The building was completed April, 1927, and is undamaged in 1935.

published every year through 1935 in the Proceedings of the American Wood Preservers' Association.

In reporting on the results of such tests, untreated check wood samples or the untreated wood of nearby buildings must be carefully watched and their conditions compared with the wood under test. In this manner constant data are available on the presence of termites and the intensity of their attack. Without this information, tests are valueless. Even untreated wood will be safe where no termites are present.

Thus far, results indicate that nowhere in the world is there grown commercial timber which is absolutely immune to attack by termites. Nevertheless, the heartwood of certain species of trees is very resistant to termites. Among the most resistant woods which were tested are teak (*Tectona grandis*) and sal (*Shorea robusta*) of India; cypress-pine (*Callitris robusta*) of Australia; camphor wood (*Cinnamomum camphora*) of the Orient; redwood (*Sequoia sempervirens*) of the Pacific Coast of the United States; southern cypress (*Taxodium distichum*) of southern United States; and species of junipers (*Juniperus* spp.) of the United States.

While the resistance of heartwood cypress is due to some chemical extractive which is repellent to termites, in the case of "pecky cypress" the resistance is due to physical causes as well, since termites do not like to work in wood where there are cavities or honeycombs. Pecky cypress is caused by a fungus or low form of plant growth which eats out pockets or chambers in the heartwood of living trees. After the tree dies or is felled this fungus also dies and the wood, although containing holes, is sound and no decay is present.

There are several reasons why termites avoid wood containing holes. First, the holes do not conserve the humidity; they permit ants and other enemies of the termites to enter; they also admit light. When working in wood, termites carefully close up such holes.

It is the presence of certain chemical constituents or extractives that renders wood termite-resistant; these resistant principles in many woods are sesquiterpene alcohols. Oils, alkaloids, gums, resins, and silica also render wood termite-resistant. Stakes of longleaf pine (*Pinus palustris*) of Texas, cut from butt logs containing a large resin content (locally called "fat-wood " or " lightwood ") remained unattacked by termites after being set in the ground exposed to their attacks from 1913 to 1932, whereas normal pine wood is very susceptible to attack by termites.

FIG. 41.   Interior view of portion of white-washed brick foundation wall of building, below ground level, showing shelter tubes of our common subterranean termite penetrating the disintegrated lime mortar. These termites came through the earth banked up against the exterior wall. To remedy this condition the exterior wall will have to be faced with concrete for some distance below the surface of the ground.

While termites do not eat mortar or plaster, they are able either by chemical or physical means to penetrate poor grades of mortar or old, disintegrating mortar (fig. 41). By means of acidulous secretions from the frontal gland, certain tropical termites (species of *Coptotermes*) are able to dissolve lime mortar.

Recognizing this, the Japanese Government prohibits the use of lime mortar in the construction of the foundations of buildings in Formosa, where termite damage is very severe.

One often hears, "Termites came right through the concrete." Apparently so, yes! In reality, no! Unless there was too much lime in the mixture, termites could not have penetrated concrete. The standard is one part Portland cement to three parts of sand to which may be added ten per cent by weight of the cement of some workability agent such as hydrated lime.

Grading stakes left down when a concrete floor was laid, spreader sticks left in a concrete wall (fig. 42), sleepers laid down in moist concrete, or defects in the concrete have all been factors where termites apparently came through concrete.

Tests of mortars and concretes of various different chemical and physical combinations, as well as of mortars with poisons included when mixed, have been conducted by the Bureau of Entomology to determine the most effective combination for foundations below the surface of the ground for the purpose of preventing penetration by termites. At Falls Church, Virginia, sixteen test walls or panels were constructed in August, 1926. Other similar test walls have been built by the Bureau of Standards at Washington, D. C., and by the State Entomologist at Urbana, Illinois, during 1927 in co-

Fig. 42. "Spreader stick" in concrete wall penetrated by native subterranean termites which reached structural timber by means of tubes.

operation with the Bureau of Entomology. These will be rather long-time tests; however, certain grades of mortars have already failed.

CHAPTER VI

GUESTS OR INQUILINES FOUND
IN TERMITE NESTS

THE writer has written much about termites which invade the homes of man and destroy his structures as well as materials stored therein. It should be interesting to discuss those foes and friends that invade the termite's own homes, which in the tropics are more or less architecturally pretentious structures, often well drained, well ventilated or air conditioned, and kept at higher temperatures and higher humidity than the environment without. There live the guests of the termites, in greatly varied relationships to their hosts. The study of this close association of dissimilar forms of life is one of the most fascinating in the whole realm of biology.

Although, in general, we may classify the forms of life found intimately associated with termites into plants and animals, the determination proves to be difficult in the case of some of the lower organisms found in the intestines of many termites. Briefly, it may be said that the associates of the termite range from single-celled plants and animals to the highest type of animal life — the mammals.

The classification of these welcome and unwelcome guests gives one a broad general view of the science of biology, since they are of both high and low estate, and a review of them presents the outline of a synoptic table of life: i.e., a chart showing the evolution of the lower to the higher forms of life and the general relationship of termites to these forms. Although the more primitive termites do not have as many or as highly modified associates as do the higher, more specialized termites, undoubtedly such association existed millions of years ago before man appeared on the planet. But in termite nests on some of the islands of the West Indies such associations have not yet been discovered.

Termite nests afford these guests hiding places, security,

greater warmth and humidity (and in desert regions a cooler retreat), abundance of a variety of food, and the combined aggressiveness of a community.

These co-inhabitants of termite nests may be classed as parasites, predators, scavengers, and various stages of " guests ". The guests — mostly insects — may be classified as to whether they are persecuted by the termites, indifferently tolerated, or eagerly cared for, fed and protected (see Addenda, Table III). Since there is no altruism, even among the social insects, it is certain that if such insect forms are cared for, in some manner they prove useful to the termites. Indeed, these highly specialized forms exchange nourishment with the termites and possess glands from which the termites obtain exudate or special liquid nourishment eagerly sought after by termites. Some of these insect guests are fearfully and wonderfully made and have extremely odd shapes.

Most of the " termitophiles " or guests in termite colonies, which live in various relationships to their host termites (see Addenda, Table III), are peculiarly modified beetles, and many are flies. Among the primitive termites but few true adapted guests have been discovered as yet. The greatest number of species and the most varied forms are found associated with the higher or more specialized species of the family Termitidae. Most inquilines, as yet, have been found in Africa; but there has been a similar but independent parallel development of peculiarly adapted or physogastric forms in all of the zoögeographical regions, or regions with the same general forms of plant and animal life. However, no matter in what regions they may occur, many have the same general aspect.

Ants have similar guests which are called " myrmecophiles " or " ant-loving "; termite guests are termed " termitophiles " or " termite-loving ".

In some cases, the inquilines superficially resemble the host termites; and this, together with their colony odor and exudate secretion, gives them protection by their hosts even when they may be preying on the young termites.

Our native termites have all classes of these guests except the specially modified or physogastric forms. Nests of nearctic termites are not so concentrated but more diffused and are less stable and more liable to changes due to environment. Hence they do not offer the safe, warm havens, well stocked with food, that occur in the tropics.

Most interesting of all, however, are those protected and cared-for physogastric guests, which are often remarkably modified; the abdomen is monstrously enlarged, or swollen, possibly by reason of the same special food which is given to the enlarged queen termites. Fly and beetle adults have greatly enlarged abdomens, and in some beetles the swollen abdomen is inverted over that portion of the body on which are the legs: these forms developing from perfectly normal larvae or young are called physogastric.

Another specialized character is the presence of peculiar lateral glands or appendages for the secretion of exudate or the special liquid nourishment so eagerly sought after by termites. Fly larvae, the caterpillars of moths, and beetle larvae have these peculiar exudate glands, which may be few or many in number and assume different shapes and varied character.

When termites migrate from one habitat to another in search of a more favorable environment, their associates migrate with the colony, as do the guests of ants. But when termites are carried accidentally by man by means of commerce from one country to another, as a rule their parasites and guests are not transported with them.

This intimate association for mutual benefit of different forms of insects with the exchange of nourishment (trophallaxis) between termites and their guests is one of the most specialized and remarkable cases of "symbiosis" (living together) in all animal life. Several distinguished entomologists have made life studies of these intriguing insects of which termites are the hosts.

Various characteristic small shell-animals or molluscs are found only in association with termites, such as *Microconus* and *Guppya* in Panama. Nothing is known as to whether there is any correlation between their lives. Others, crustaceans called "pill bugs", having no definite shells (Isopods), are specially modified and also exist only in association with termites. Millipeds, modified in form, also live only in association with termites; and centipeds occur in colonies.

The primitive springtails and "silverfish" or lepismids are among the most lowly insect associates of termites or termitophiles; they are probably merely scavengers.

It even happens that some termites live with others, usually in special galleries in the exterior of the nest; they probably are of some benefit as scavengers. Several species may thus live in the same mound nest in the tropics. Species of *Termitaphis* occur free in the galleries with the ter-mites; and this peculiar flat, round hemipterous insect is fairly rapidly mov-ing. The *Termitaphis* has been found in many colonies of certain termites at vari-ous localities in the Neotropical region; these colonies were in logs or branches lying on the moist ground. These insects may be predaceous.

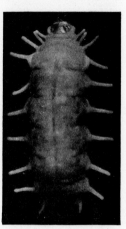

Some beetles with oddly modified larvae or young are normal in the adult winged state. A ladybird-beetle (a coccinelid — *Ortalistes rubidus* Gorham) found in tree nests in Panama has the larva modified and is a cared-for guest. The larvae ex-hibit the same convulsive jerky move-ments shown by termites when alarmed. The adult is not different from the nor-mal type of beetle.

An association of the modified young of a histerid beetle was recently found in the carton tree nest of a Costa Rican ter-

FIG. 43. Larva or young of a preda-ceous histerid beetle found in a carton nest of a Costa Rican termite. Note exu-date glands at sides of body. Greatly en-larged.

mite. These beetles are predaceous and are certainly wolves in sheep's clothing (fig. 43).

Some of the insects are closely associated with the queens of the termites; one small beetle rests on the body of the queen of a termite (*Reticulitermes lucifugus* Rossi) in the United States. When removed, it always eagerly returns to its perch on the queen.

The eggs of beetle or fly termitophiles are sometimes found attached to the legs of termite queens in South American species from tree nests. In India, dark red globular eggs of spider-like (acarid) animals are found among the egg masses of fungus-growing termites in mound nests.

There is an interesting biological relationship between cer-tain tropical American termites which build carton tree nests and stingless bees (species of *Trigona*). The small bees build their nests and honeycomb within the nests of the termites, often in the center, and take over a large portion of the termite nest structure; the bees have a separate funnel-shaped entrance to their part of the nest. Anyone disturbing such a termite nest is assailed by swarms of these bees, which, while they cannot sting, do bite and are able to penetrate under clothing, into hair, etc., making one extremely uncomfortable.

Large wasps (species of *Megachile* and *Euglossa*) often construct their mud cells in the outer layers or walls of mound termite nests in Panama.

Wasp-like parasitic insects (*Termitobracon* sp.) have been found in termite nests and are very probably parasitic on some of the insects living with the termites; their young have never been found as parasites in the bodies of termites.

An ant, *Camponotus novegranadense* Mayr, inhabits the carton tree nests of termites in Panama. This ant is pacific, has its own galleries, and does not molest and is not molested by these termites.

Especially interesting is the large reptile — the Nile monitor — which breaks into and lays its eggs in the interior of termite nests and leaves them there to hatch, where there is maintained by the termites a constant temperature and humidity, for the termites at once repair the break made in the nest by the reptile.

Certain parrot-like birds also excavate their nest holes in the carton tree nests of ants and termites, in Middle and South America. Young birds are reared in such nests!

It will be seen that various types of termite nests are also made use of by many other forms of life which find these nests convenient havens. Vegetation of various kinds may cover mound nests of termites, or the mound and several feet at the base may be bare of vegetation.

To summarize, the various forms of life found associated with termites come under several categories, namely: parasites; predators; scavengers; those forms which merely seek a protected haven; and, most important, the modified forms which exchange nourishment with the termites.

Is not the study of the termites — true " social insects " — worthy of more attention, and is the enthusiasm of the small band of their devotees to be wondered at? Many of the greatest marvels of nature are to be observed in the smaller forms of life!

CHAPTER VII

THE DISTURBANCE OF THE BALANCE
OF NATURE BY MAN

CHANGES, either natural or artificial, in a life community may so disturb it as to eliminate forms of life or force changes in habits or habitats. Life is so interrelated that often but little change will disturb this delicate " balance of nature ". In the Hawaiian Islands, which are of volcanic origin, only the older and more widespread fauna and flora may be termed native or endemic. Most forms of life have been introduced and are exotic, or of foreign origin. Man has developed sugar-cane (and later, pineapple) plantations over extensive areas of land. As is usual where large crops of the same plant are grown, serious infestations by insects occur and epidemics arise. " Pure " cultivation of one plant over large areas without intermingling or mixing with others gives plant-feeding insects a wonderful opportunity to multiply and spread. Such concentrations of special food are seldom found in nature, especially not in the tropical regions.

To protect the valuable sugar crop the Hawaiian planters formed a protective research association which employed entomologists to scour those regions of the world where sugar-cane grows to find parasites of the insect enemies of this crop. They were so successful that now an artificial balance of nature has been established and the parasites keep in check the plant-feeding insects.

Hence, if one desires to introduce new birds or animals into Hawaii, careful study of their habits must be made before permission is granted. Nothing must disturb this balance of nature, or the plant feeders might again become epidemic.

In the days of the North American Indian, termites were at least somewhat beneficial as scavengers in the widespread areas of forest land. While their value was not as great in reducing the dead wood of fallen trees or stumps into plant food as that of low forms of plant life which cause rot or decay, termites were

PLATE IV. Damage to citrus trees by *Neotermes castaneus* Burm. in southern Florida.

Above: Split in the bark of a grapefruit tree, where termite galleries come near the surface; this characteristic splitting of the bark is about the only outside sign of termites working in a tree. These cankers appeared about 18 months before the pictures were taken.

Below: Termite galleries in the trunk and roots of a grapefruit tree.

an important factor. Both rot and termites were able to break down cellulose into available form in the soil for plant food.

Since the advent of the white man and the clearing of forests and the cultivation of the land, termites have been gradually becoming more and more of a pest to crops, buildings, and other works.

Even today, however, termites are of aid to man in eating stumps on land cleared for agricultural purposes in the tropics, so that they later can be removed from the fields; natives of the Philippines find termites of great help in this rôle. Nevertheless, termites are destructive to living trees in tea, rubber, and teak plantations in the Orient.

Thus we see that the reason that termite damage becomes more of a problem with advancing civilization is the disturbance of the balance of nature by man. With the felling of the forests and the clearing and cultivation of the land, the natural breeding places of termites in dead trees and plant roots have been destroyed. Damage to buildings has resulted, and due to the fact that there have been more extensive building operations, and also that there has been improper, " speculative " building, there has been at least an apparent increase in termite damage. Also, due to general educational progress, termite damage is not so frequently confused with " dry rot " either by craftsmen or the general public; the public is becoming more " termite conscious." With modern stone and steel construction in cities and more durable foundations for frame dwellings there should be a decrease in termite damage to the woodwork of buildings.

TERMITES AND FUNGI. Wood-destroying fungi cannot live in wood containing less than the 12 to 15 per cent moisture normally contained in air-dried wood; but dry-wood termites (Kalotermitidae) can survive in wood with smaller moisture content. Hence, these termites are not dependent upon fungi to break down cellulose into available forms of food.

The relationship of free-living wood-destroying fungi with termites in wood presents a problem which is rather obscure at the present time. Undoubtedly, there is a more definite interrelationship between the rotten wood termite of the Pacific Coast and the wood-destroying fungi than occurs in the other types of termites. With regard to the more destructive subterranean termites and the dry-wood termites (the latter can ap-

PLATE V.   *Above:* Termites have been found in limbs eight to nine feet from the ground, the galleries extending into the trunk and roots.
Below: Damage to the trunk and roots of a grapefruit tree.   *Photos. by W. L. Thompson, Agric. Exper. Station, University of Florida.*

parently work in wood which is too dry for fungi to live in) ,
the problem is more complex and the interrelationship is but
little understood. I do not believe that any termites are entirely
dependent on fungi to break down wood for food. Subterranean termites and types of dry-wood termites can destroy wood
without the assistance of free-living fungi, and wood-destroying
fungi can likewise destroy wood without the assistance of termites.

Even though subterranean termites and fungi are each capable of independently destroying wood, they often work together. It may be that there is an association for even greater
and quicker efficiency in obtaining the destruction of wood. It
will take much careful research work to prove or disprove this.

According to Dr. Cleveland, of Harvard University, no work
has demonstrated the necessity of fungi in wood in order to
make it usable or digestible for termites. Wood-destroying
fungi live in wood where termites are unknown, as in Alaska,
just as they do in those regions where termites occur. The
partial destruction of wood by fungi no doubt makes the wood
easier for certain termites to eat, but many termites eat only
sound, dry wood in which the destructive action of fungi is
reduced to a minimum. Some termites feed only on the wood
of living trees.

On the other hand, it is definitely known that termites can
live for many months on cellulose of the highest purity. Their
intestinal protozoa contain cellulose. It can be demonstrated
that in the absence of bacteria and fungi cellulose disappears
from termites within twenty-four hours after the protozoa are
removed, and does not reappear until the protozoa are replaced.
The termites die unless these protozoa are replaced. Hence,
we may conclude that the intestinal protozoa of termites are
primarily responsible for the digestion of the cellulose content
of the wood that termites eat.

It is to dead vegetation that termites usually turn. Where
logs, stumps, and roots of weed vegetation are no longer available in cleared land, they may attack crops. With the destruction by man of their natural homes in forest and field, termites
have also been forced to attack buildings, in order to obtain
food and shelter from the woodwork of such buildings. A
beam in an improperly constructed building is merely a dead
tree branch; and an untreated telegraph pole, a log on end.

From forest and field scavengers, termites have become pests to man, largely because of careless construction, without precautions against termites.

Likewise in carrying on the pure culture of crops man has made cellulose or wood more easily available to termites in his structures of wood grouped in ranches, villages, and cities. Highways for termite advance across treeless plains and desert regions have been made available in lines of fence posts — in once unfenced areas — and in the transcontinental telephone and power pole lines.

The Bureau of Entomology of the United States Department of Agriculture has made a thorough country-wide study of the problem and finds that the public has several misconceptions in regard to termite damage to buildings. These popular errors are: that termites have been introduced into this country and are spreading; that they can be killed by insecticides or fumigants, as can true ants; that the disappearance of the winged adults of "flying ants" is an end of the injury to the woodwork of the building and its contents. "Recent", "spreading", "introduced", are terms frequently applied by the misinformed to our native termites, which have been on the North American continent far longer than man. As has been shown, termites inhabit temperate regions of the world, as well as the tropics, where, however, they are more numerous and conspicuous.

Species of *Reticulitermes,* our own common subterranean termites, range around the world in the north temperate zone. Studies of fossils, previously discussed, have revealed that in prehistoric times they were even more widely distributed. We have records of their occurrence not only in shale rocks of the United States, many millions of years old, but also in Baltic amber from the bottom of the Baltic Sea.

Changes in environment, to which they could not adapt themselves, have led to their present more limited distribution.

Recently, however, in widely separated localities, certain puzzling cases of damage to very old buildings have occurred. These houses, ranging from one hundred to two hundred years of age, had never before been attacked. These cases have led competent observers such as Dr. H. von Schrenk of St. Louis, Missouri, to believe that there may be "biologic waves" or cycles of greater activity by termites. This theory is somewhat borne out by examinations of early colonial houses in Virginia, where damage had occurred and been repaired, and the wood apparently abandoned and then reattacked.

Possibly factors of environment are involved which are not immediately apparent or not at all noticeable by man. Changes in climate, sub-soil conditions, etc., could thus account for sudden local increases in termite damage, and yet be too subtle to be detected by man. Such changes would also explain why termites abandon nests in wood and elsewhere, when the food supply and other conditions are apparently favorable.

More easily understandable is the recent lowering of the water table at New Orleans, Louisiana, to secure prompt and proper drainage, which has resulted in greater damage to the woodwork of buildings by subterranean termites (*Reticulitermes*); formerly the soil was too wet, due to the nearness of the water to the surface of the ground.

Irrigation of desert and prairie areas in southwestern United States also creates more favorable conditions for termite persistence and advance, and renders available a larger supply of more succulent food than nature's former meager supply.

Large areas of the Canal Zone in Panama were cleared of termites by the formation of Gatun Lake; in the building of the Panama Canal, subterranean termites were eradicated from the soil by the flooding of the land. Even colonies of species of *Nasutitermes* in carton nests on dead standing trees in the lake died out, possibly due to the direct exposure to the sun's rays, or lack of food in the form of vegetation. Colonies in similar carton nests in jungle swamps are in thriving condition.

The agricultural development of the American tropics and the clearing off of the dense tropical jungle growth for banana, pineapple, avocado, and cacao plantations have resulted in the killing of many termite colonies of species that require the moist habitat of the jungle. The intense heat of the tropical sun will render the decaying logs, stumps, and branches on the ground and even the soil too dry and unsuitable for these termites.

Thus man's operations can change the habits and habitats of termites, and, in some cases of great topographical alterations, can even change the character of the termite fauna of an area.

CHAPTER VIII

DAMAGE BY TERMITES TO THE WOODWORK
OF BUILDINGS, BOATS, POLES,
MINE PROPS, ETC.

WITH their long experience as practical and successful builders, wood-destroying termites have no difficulty in finding weak points in the construction of the buildings of man. Driven from their homes in the forest by land clearing, cultivation, and advancing civilization, termites have become destructive to man's handiwork. Such ability of termites to destroy is recognized by the colored folk of the southern states, who hang "white ants" in a bag around the neck of a teething child to help it "cut" teeth. Did our negroes bring this folk-lore from their original home in tropical Africa, where termites are much more common and destructive?

Careless building, or construction without regard to possible damage by termites, not only jeopardizes the integrity of the structure, but also renders liable to injury the contents of the building. While this serious damage and loss can be prevented by proper construction of buildings, it is very difficult to get rid of termites when once they have infested a building.

Few people realize the large amount of damage caused to the woodwork of buildings by wood-destroying termites, or "white ants", in the United States. Such destruction, with the necessary repairs and replacements, is roughly estimated to cost forty million dollars a year. This damage, in both cities and rural regions, is due primarily to the improper construction of buildings. Accurate figures on the actual damage to buildings by termites over our extensive country are lacking; there have been partial surveys in but a few cities. There has been great exaggeration of the amount and seriousness of termite damage by commercial termite control operators.

During the fiscal year ending June 30, 1932, 1650 cases of termite damage to buildings were reported to the federal Bureau

of Entomology; 2075 was the total the following fiscal year ending June 30, 1933, and 2532 during the fiscal year ending June
30, 1934. These represent a mere fraction of the cases actually
discovered during that period and these again are but a small
fraction of those actually in existence. For example, according
to the Termite Investigations Committee of the University of
California, from November 1930 to August 15, 1931 the reported cases of repair in Los Angeles County alone totalled 1840;
and these, of course, by no means represent the total number of
cases of termite damage for that area and period.

The number of such cases seems to be controlled by several
factors, chiefly (1) latitude (especially temperature and humidity), (2) altitude, (3) population, (4) general education
of the public, and (5) activity of commercial termite control
operators. Factors leading to periodic changes are 4 and 5 and
the lowering of water tables and artificial irrigation in the southwestern United States.

While the most serious structural damage and the most common and widespread injury to buildings and their contents is
caused by subterranean termites, along the southern seacoast
considerable damage is caused by the non-subterranean type.
Large public and other buildings in Key West, Miami, Palm
Beach, and Tampa, Florida; New Orleans, Louisiana; Browns-
ville, Texas; Savannah, Georgia; Charleston, South Carolina;
and less commonly elsewhere, have been more or less severely
damaged by dry-wood termites. Similar damage to furniture
by dry-wood termites has also been observed in these and other
cities.

Many investigations made by the biologists of the Termite
Investigations Committee of the University of California in different cities and towns in California have shown that termites
could be found in from twenty to ninety per cent of residences
of the ordinary type, or, if not in them, in some wooden structures on the premises, such as poles, posts, fences, walks, flower
stakes, etc.

It has been found profitable to protect wooden buildings from
termites by an additional investment of from 2 to 10%; this
means, over fifty years of depreciation, from 0.04% to 0.2% per
annum. The higher protection insurance or figure is additional
cost in construction to prevent damage by dry-wood termites.

Since damage by these termites in continental United States is not widespread or serious, this additional cost is not warranted, at least in this country, from the standpoint of protection against termites alone, but would have to include protection against decay and fire as well as termites.

Buildings of many different types and kinds are damaged by termites. Adobe houses, barns, bridges, log cabins, churches, derricks, dry docks, engine roundhouses, factories, ferry houses, garages, federal (fig. 44) and state government buildings, grain elevators, granaries, greenhouses, hospitals, hotels, dwelling houses or residences, icehouses, lighthouses, mills, observatories,

Fig. 44. Damage to a temporary government building by subterranean termites at Washington, D. C.

office buildings, outhouses, notable public buildings, rammed earth buildings, sheds, silos, storage houses, wharves, windmill towers, etc., are some of the many diverse structures that have been invaded by termites.

We have seen how the disturbance of the balance of nature by man in clearing land has changed the habits of termites. In addition, there has been a period between the old, well constructed dwelling, in which the best of materials were carefully used, and the modern steel and concrete buildings or frame buildings with impenetrable foundations, when mass and speculative building and the use of poor grades of materials resulted

in greater termite damage.   Furthermore, some authorities believe there are periodic rises and drops in the activity of termites
or " biologic waves " — cycles of greater damage.

Subterranean termites gain entrance to buildings from colonies out of doors, and since the workers can extend subterranean
galleries for comparatively long distances, it is often impossible
to trace the insects to the outside source.   These termites are
not brought into the buildings in lumber used in construction.
This is a fallacious argument used in discriminating against the
use of wood as a construction material.   It is not the use of wood,
but improper construction that leads to infestation by subterranean termites.

Often termite damage to wood is mistaken for that caused by
rot or decay, which is actually produced by quite different organisms, namely, low forms of plant life or fungi, which also
destroy wood.   Sometimes both these insects and decay cause
damage to the same structure at the same time.   Where products
such as lumber are damaged after being put in place, the cost of
replacement involves additional loss of labor and time, as well
as the cost of the original and replaced products, a loss far greater
than the value of the raw products.   Often such replacement
expenses should be attributed to both wood-destroying fungi and
wood-boring insects and not to one agency alone, as frequently
there is a close relationship between these forms of life in the
destruction of timber.   Either, however, is capable of doing the
damage alone.   Termites cannot extract food from wood in advanced stages of decay, since the fungi have already assimilated
its nutritive value.

Boats and other vessels may be classed as dwelling places for
man.   Both the subterranean and dry-wood types of termites
attack vessels.   In southern Florida probably more cases of such
infestation by " powder-post " termites occur than anywhere
else in this country.

In Hawaii, a coal barge became infested by subterranean termites which obtained the necessary water from dirt and moisture in the bottom.   The barge became infested by winged adult
termites flying to it from the heavily infested water front.   A
floating dry dock at Honolulu became similarly infested.   A
passenger boat plying between Hawaii and California became
infested with this same termite working in wood kept moist by

water leakage. Extensive repairs were necessary, not only to stop
further damage to the boat but also to prevent the introduction
of this exotic oriental termite into continental United States.
Winged adults from the ship could easily reach the shore.

In the days of the wooden warships, several became infested by
tropical termites and these old vessels were seriously damaged
or destroyed. It is reported that a captured slaver condemned
and dismantled at Jamestown led to the infestation of the Island
of St. Helena by a destructive Brazilian subterranean termite
unknown on this island before 1840.

In addition to damage to buildings and boats, termites injure
wooden beehives, tree boxes, bridge piling and timbers, underground lead-sheathed cables, chicken coops, conduits, docks,
dog kennels, mine props, wooden paving blocks, piling, tent pins,
wooden pipe lines, telephone and telegraph poles, electric light
or power poles, including cross-arms and wooden insulator pegs,
hop and bean poles, ridge poles of tents, posts and fencing, railway ties, wharves, etc.

Almost all of the works or crops of man are subject to damage,
especially any timbers in contact with the ground.

Damage to mine props, poles, and fence posts by subterranean
termites is of considerable economic importance; in many parts
of the United States the poles and posts are attacked by both subterranean and dry-wood termites. Damage to untreated poles,
both to the bases and to the tops, by dry-wood termites has been
observed in Florida, Georgia, South Carolina, Alabama, Mississippi, Louisiana, Texas, and California. In reality, poles, mine
props and posts are merely logs (barked or unbarked) stood on
end in the earth in a new surrounding.

Damage to railway ties where there is a good stone ballast and
heavy traffic is unknown. It is believed that the vibration is disturbing to these insects, and they will not inhabit railway ties
for this reason. Some damage to ties in earth on rural lines or
street railways has been discovered. All such damage has been
caused by subterranean termites. In Sinai damage to ties by
dry-wood termites has been reported.

Since 1909, the writer has conducted special investigations of
damage to both treated and untreated telephone poles for the
federal Bureau of Entomology in cooperation with pole-using
corporations. These studies made in different sections of the

country are the basis for the suggestions for preventing damage which are outlined later.

As a result of similar investigations, I found that in the southern states the principal insect injury to mine props and other timbers in slope or incline mines is caused by termites. Timbers placed on the heavily timbered slope or incline, extending from 250 to 300 feet from the exterior into the mine, are attacked by termites, as are those used in "headings" near the surface of the ground. Individuals of the winged form enter the mine and establish colonies at the bases of the props. The moist conditions of the prop at the base, where the wood is in contact with the ground and where there is usually incipient decay, offers especially favorable conditions for injury by this class of insects.

The presence of these insects in mine props is not easily detected. Their work is hidden beneath an outer shell of wood, often very thin, but always left intact; therefore ordinary inspection of the exterior of the props will not reveal the presence of the insects or their destructive work. The entire interior may be completely honeycombed while there is nothing on the exterior to indicate the injury.

Treatment with wood preservatives will prevent injury, but the method and the preservative used depend on the length of service desired and the extent to which the owner is willing to go.

As pointed out, damage by subterranean termites is more common, widespread, and serious than that caused by the dry-wood type. They have sought food and shelter in the structures of man and as a result buildings and their contents, wooden poles, derricks, towers, posts, ties, and mine props are damaged. Minor local injury occurs to trees, shrubs, crops, and flowers.

DAMAGE TO STORED MATERIAL

Of the stored material sometimes seriously injured or destroyed by termites may be mentioned wooden electrotype blocks, books or papers in libraries or elsewhere, valuable documents, wood-pulp products, pasteboard, rolls of cloth and other fabrics, clothing, shoes and other leather products, and food stored on shelves or on the floors in dark, damp basements or cellars, or in similar moist places where the ventilation is poor (Plate VI).

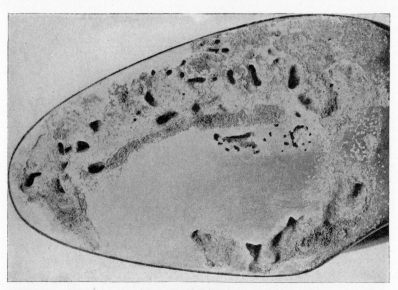

PLATE VI. Shoe damaged by subterranean termites because it was stored on wooden shelving in a building infested by these insects. Shotgun shells similarly damaged from infested wooden shelving.

I have said that the termites are selective feeders. This is true: much material damaged is not eaten but is merely bored through or corroded with moisture or frontal gland secretion because it happened to be in the way or must be penetrated in order to reach food or to permit the emergence of the winged adults. This must be kept in mind while reading about the different types of building material, stored products, vegetation, etc., injured or destroyed by termites.

The following is an incomplete list of the varied materials or products which have been damaged by termites in this country and in the tropics; also included are some of the more odd or very unusual types of injury:

Fig. 45. Damage to a wet battery by native subterranean termites.

Airplanes in sheds, asphalt, balls (composition billiard, croquet, golf, and tennis), bamboo poles, bandages, barrels, baseball bats, wet battery containing sulphuric acid (fig. 45), beans, plant benches, Bibles (covers and text), blue prints, bonds, bones (eroded), books, boxes (wood and cardboard or carton), bridges, cables (under ground), canvas, carpets, packing-cases, chests, clocks, cloth, clothing, coffins, coins (eroded when buried for safe keeping in the soil in China), composition board, conduits, cord, cork, cork insulation board, cotton bales, drawing boards, electrical equipment, electrotype blocks, file baskets, boxes or cases, fruit piled on the ground, furniture (beds, bookcases, iceboxes, bureaus, chairs, desks, tables, X-Ray cabinets, washstands, etc.), furs, glass (eroded), grain, guns (wood eaten and metal corroded in the Philippines — Plate VIII), hose

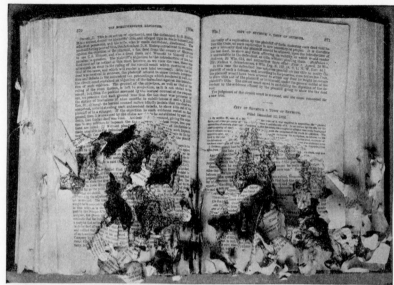

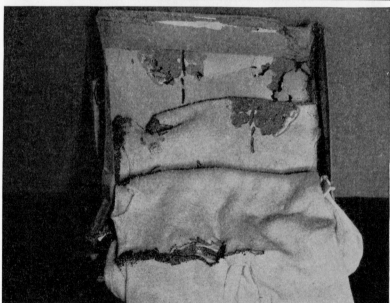

PLATE VII. Book from bookcase indirectly attacked by termites from wooden flooring which they were eating. Children's underwear, damaged by termites, stored on infested shelving in a building improperly constructed.

(cotton-jacketed rubber fire hose), insulation (sawdust in ice houses full of ice; rubber and tar cloth on wires or cables; and insulation or wallboard of wood pulp or fiber), insulator pegs, ivory elephant tusks (in storage in Africa marred by grooving), labels, lead, leather, linoleum, linotype blocks, lime mortar (between bricks in the foundation of buildings), logs (imported), lumber (in piles), mummies (in graves in Egypt), nuts, organs, pasteboard, pews (in churches), phonograph records, photographs, plans (of vessels in navy yard), plywood, pianos, pictures, picture frames, wall plaster, post-cards, potatoes (Irish and sweet), powder (gunpowder, both black and smokeless, stored in boxes), radios, railway cars (freight and passenger, in Hawaii), ribbon belting, rollers (shade), rugs, flour sacks, seeds, sewing machines, shotgun shells (Plate VI), shelves, shoes, silos, skulls (eroded in graves), stamps (postage and revenue), staves, sticks (label), water tanks, tar and tar-paper (used in waterproofing), tile (artificial composition), ties (railway), toy (rag dog in Panama), tin cans (in Singapore, containing kerosene oil, eroded so that oil leaked out), trunks, plant tubs, twine, typewriters, underwear, victrolas, wallboard, wall paper, rubber washers on fruit jars, wool, yarn, and yeast cakes (in Texas).

There is evidence that termites not only injure man's habitations while he is alive but also infest the last resting place of man on this earth, namely, the caskets and coffins of the dead. Termites frequently and in many localities have been observed swarming from the earth in cemeteries. They often burrow far below the surface deep into the earth, following the woodwork of wells or the wooden forms on concrete work, as in the locks of the Panama Canal, where they caused damage to electric cables. The eroding of bones and skulls has been observed in Egypt, Nubia, and China. This, however, is not a very cheerful subject. Neither was it very pleasant to be called into consultation at a hospital where termites were damaging wooden iceboxes containing human cadavers with the strong odor of formaldehyde present.

DAMAGE TO LIVING VEGETATION

DAMAGE TO FRUIT, NUT, SHADE, AND FOREST TREES. Subterranean termites occasionally injure living trees and shrubs. In

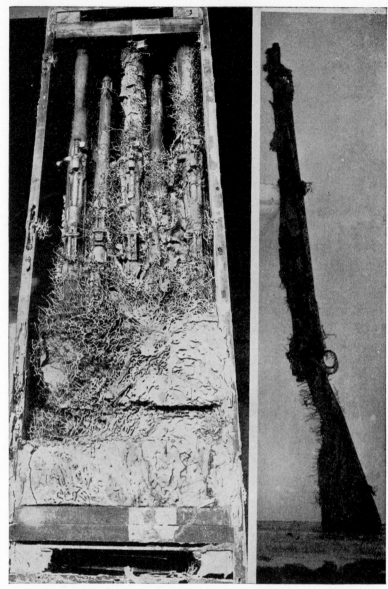

PLATE VIII. Guns in cases stored on cracked concrete floor damaged by subterranean termites in the Philippines; the wood is eaten, and the metal is corroded.

Florida they have caused considerable damage to newly planted groves of orange trees, having eaten away the bark about the collar and root and completely girdled the trees. Similar damage by termites has been recorded to other fruit trees, as apple, peach, pear, cherry, plum, apricot, lemon, and guava, especially in the southern states and in California; and also to pecan, chestnut, and walnut trees. Such damage is more common in the new soil of recently cleared woodland containing old decaying stumps or much humus. As a rule, such injury is only occasional and local.

There is some damage by termites to fruit which has dropped and is lying on the ground: grapefruit, oranges, and pears have so been eaten into and ruined, but such damage is too occasional to be serious.

In cities and elsewhere many varieties of shade trees are injured by termites, the insects infesting the roots and the heartwood at the base of injured trees. Sometimes the infested trees are plastered with earth-like tubes or galleries.

Particularly in the South, termites render insect, fire, and disease-killed timber unmerchantable, unless the timber is utilized within a reasonable period after being killed. They also damage the roots and lower trunks of injured living trees, or trees scarred by fire. The dead heartwood of trees may be eaten out to heights of fifty feet, even in living trees. In the tropics shelter tubes are constructed up the trunks of trees to great heights.

Dry-wood termites injure fruit and ornamental trees in the southern states and in California, especially citrus trees (Plate III). Species of *Neotermes,* or " damp wood " termites, and the closely related *Paraneotermes* cause the most serious injury: the roots, trunks, and branches are attacked, usually through some scar. These particular non-subterranean or dry-wood — in reality " damp wood " — termites appear to be able to travel short distances through the soil and enter trees through the roots. Palm trees are damaged by species of *Kalotermes* in southern California.

DAMAGE TO NURSERY STOCK, YOUNG PLANTATION STOCK, AND VINEYARDS. There are numerous records of subterranean termite injury to young fruit and nut tree seedlings in nurseries, to other nursery stock, and to young trees planted in recently cleared ground or soil rich in humus. The injury, however, has been only occasional and not extensive. The stock is usually attacked at a scar, where the roots have been injured or cut off, or at a graft, as cleft-graft apple stock.

Injury by termites to vineyards has been occasionally recorded in North America, especially in California. Usually only the old vines are attacked, or dead or injured parts. Signs of attack are sickly foliage or abortive buds; or the injury may be observed when cutting down to stock or grafting.

DAMAGE TO SHRUBS, FLOWERS, AND GREENHOUSE STOCK. Termites injure a variety of shrubs, weeds, and flowers in gardens as well as in greenhouses under glass where the warm, moist atmosphere maintained throughout the year promotes greatly the activity of the insects. Injury from termites is especially common where the plants are perennial and have woody stalks.

SOURCES OF INFESTATION. Heavily manured flower beds are a source of infestation to the stems of the flowers, as well as to the woodwork of buildings near by, if suitable protection is lacking. Untreated wooden stakes used as supports often become infested, and in time the insects attack the plants. In greenhouses termites often attack old label sticks, the wooden uprights supporting wooden benches set on or in the ground, and the wooden bench bottoms and plant pots, and later attack the growing plants. The insects come up through the ground and form dirt galleries over the supports, or burrow up through the wooden bench legs and run galleries the full length of the benches. They enter the soil in the pots through the drainage holes and eat out the main stalk of the root, killing the plant very quickly.

There are records from various sections of the country of serious injury to many plants grown under glass. Heliotropes, begonias, bedding geraniums, chrysanthemums, poinsettia, and roses have been found to be seriously injured by termites. One hundred and eighty out of one thousand heliotrope plants have been killed the first week after being potted from the seeding pans. As many as 75 termites have been found in a 4-inch pot of heliotrope. Cosmos, jasmine, pansies, and oleander have been similarly damaged or killed.

DAMAGE TO FIELD CROPS AND GRAZING LAND. In the southern states termites occasionally injure the stems and roots of a great variety of apparently healthy field crops, including both grain and truck crops, among which may be listed corn, cotton, sugar-cane, rice, grasses, potatoes — both Irish and sweet — and a great variety of garden vegetables or truck crops. Included are artichokes, beans, beets, cabbage, carrots, cranberries, peanuts, rhubarb, squash, turnips, etc., as well as cantaloupe and similar melons.

Injury to corn in the prairie region of Kansas has resulted from the earlier presence of the insects in enormous quantities in the heavily sodded soil, where they feed on the roots of the vegetation. Sometimes this injury to growing corn is due also to the practice of plowing under old stubble.

In the prairie and desert regions of Texas, Arizona, and California, tube-forming termites (desert termites), live in the ground, feeding on the roots of grass and other vegetation, and are often found under and within dry cow dung and under stones. These species sometimes destroy the vegetation over large areas of grazing land. One of the characteristic habits is to cover the stems and roots of vegetation with tubes of small diameter, constructed of earth and excrement, to induce decay in the covered portions, and make them digestible by termites.

CHAPTER IX

BIOLOGICAL CONTROL OF TERMITES

PARASITES. Because of their life in darkness, underground or hidden within wood, in earth-like shelter tubes, or in carton nests, and because of their constant activity, termites are among the very few forms of insect life which do not harbor internal insect parasites. Most other insects are parasitized by wasp-like insects which so reduce their numbers as to afford a natural check to their spread. These insect parasites are usually an important factor in the biological control of an insect species.

With the exception of the larvae of a conopid fly found parasitic in the heads of one species of termite (*Macrotermes gilvus* Hagen) in the Oriental region, no insect larvae have been found within the bodies of termites anywhere in the world. These fly larvae apparently do not kill the termites but only cause " myiasis " or injury. The heads of the infested termites are so distorted, however, that one prominent entomologist, before this fact was known, described and classified such infested termites as two new species in a genus new to science (*Gnathotermes*), whereas in reality they were merely a known species structurally modified and arrested in development by the larvae of the fly.

Round worms or thread-like nematodes internally infest the heads of termites, in this country and elsewhere, and occur in sick and dead termites; apparently they do not serve as an effective natural check to the increase of termites under natural conditions. In South Africa a nematode infests " harvesting " termites or species of *Hodotermes* which come above ground and crawl about in search of food in the sunlight. Fowls eat such infested termites and in turn become infested with the injurious nematode.

Mites of various odd shapes cling externally to the bodies of termites; usually they are in the young or migratory stage and apparently they are not able to kill healthy termites under normal conditions.   Sometimes they occur in numbers: indeed, in artificial colonies in the laboratory they may become so numerous as to cause the death of the termites.   The external attachment of small mites to the bodies of termites is often very symmetrical, as if there were some effort to distribute or balance the load, i.e., " trim ship "!

Low forms of plant life infect the bodies of termites, but except for a few species of moulds these affect only a small percentage of the entire colony; and no epidemics result which kill off large numbers of the insects. Often the fruiting bodies of these low forms of fungi (species of *Termitaria*) are of peculiar shape: they may form narrow grayish bands with black, scalloped, turned-up edges on various parts of the insects, such as abdomen, legs, head, etc.   Quite a few species occur throughout the world, and our native termites are so infected (fig. 46) .

FIG. 46. Worker of native subterranean termite infected with a fungus disease (*Termitaria* sp.). Enlarged.

A very odd form of such a fungus found on termites inhabiting islands in the South Seas consists of a blackish oval band in the center of which there is a conical tube curved down like a briar at the tip.

Still lower forms of plant life, namely moulds and bacteria, appear to be the only effective checks in nature on the increase of termites.   Such diseases will rapidly wipe out whole colonies, both in nature and in artificial colonies.   In them, apparently, is man's best natural ally against termites; moulds and predators are important in the biological control of termites.

PREDATORS.   The dominant ants, armed fore and aft with jaws and sting, are the worst enemies of termites, which have their only weapons on the head, namely jaws and the tube or gland from which exudes a sticky defensive fluid, very effective against ants.   In Australia armies of ants break into mound nests of termites; the termites retreat into the interior and wall off with nest material the invading ants, but the ants are usually able to completely or partially take over the nest.   Marauding ants eat termites, and raids on termite nests are often for the purpose of obtaining food.   Even such primitive termites as *Cryptotermes* spp., living in wood, wall off any openings with excreted pellets of digested wood (fig. 29) , as a defense against invasion.

Termites and ants can and do live together peacefully in separate parts of the same carton nest, but each insect has its own galleries. If such a nest is broken into by man, however, the ants usually fall upon the termites, which are helpless when exposed. Indeed, ants are responsible for the present hidden life of termites: they have proven such effective predators that the soft-bodied termites have been forced to " dig in " for defense and lead an under-cover existence. While ants are the worst enemies of termites and have driven them under cover, yet ants and termites live side by side; in nature termites have not been exterminated. Ants are negligible as a control of termites.

FIG. 47. Spider-like solpugid, which behaves like a soldier termite, found in carton nest of a termite (*Mirotermes panamaensis* Sny.) in Panama. Natural size 0.6 inch. *Photo. by J. Zetek.*

Argentine ants are a menace to orchards in our southern states and in California; they also prey on termites. However, they are not a factor to be considered in any plans of man for termite control. Argentine ants must be wiped out and nothing in a termite control plan should interfere with state and federal plans for the control of Argentine ants.

Due to moulds or ants, colonies are sometimes wiped out under natural conditions. Where termites attack buildings, there have been several cases in which, after doing some or considerable damage, the termites have been exterminated either by disease or by unfavorable environmental conditions not apparent to man.

Termites are most exposed to predaceous animal life at the time of the annual swarming, which may be by day or night. Many forms of both wild and domesticated animals are attracted by the cloud of flying insects and congregate from wide areas to places from which termites are swarming. Here they gorge themselves in a gargantuan feast. Birds of many kinds, domestic fowls, reptiles, lizards, chameleons, toads, ants, spiders, solpugids (fig. 47) , predaceous wasps and flies, crickets, etc. prey upon termites at this time.

The United States Biological Survey has found that termites constitute part of the food of at least 52 species of native birds.

Birds not only prey upon termites at the time of swarming, but also dig them out of wood and the earth. The woodpeckers are represented in the list by 8 species; and as many as 1,100 termites have been found in the stomach of a common flicker. The flicker, however, is not so great a termite eater as the pileated woodpecker, termites having been found in but 15 of 720 flicker stomachs while 28 of 113 stomachs of pileated woodpeckers contained termites, one of them holding 400. Other birds consuming noteworthy numbers of termites are the Gambel quail (largest number found in one stomach, 500), Florida jay (468), roadrunner (over 300), nighthawk (220), chimney swift (160), white-necked raven (125), black swift (90).

The complete list of known nearctic bird enemies of termites follows, the most important being indicated by bold-face type: Wood duck, **bobwhite**, Arizona scaled quail, chestnut-bellied scaled quail, **Gambel's quail**, mountain plover, least sandpiper, short-billed gull, laughing gull, **roadrunner**, whip-poor-will, **nighthawk**, black swift, **chimney swift**, Vaux's swift, **flicker**, red-shafted flicker, gilded flicker, **pileated woodpecker**, hairy woodpecker, downy woodpecker, Nuttall's woodpecker, red-cockaded woodpecker, kingbird, Cassin's kingbird, black phoebe, western wood pewee, **horned lark**, tree swallow, bank swallow, barn swallow, Florida jay, white necked raven, crow, dipper, Carolina wren, mockingbird, catbird, Palmer's thrasher, woodthrush, bluebird, white-rumped shrike, yellow-throated vireo, Cape May warbler, black-throated blue warbler, pine warbler, **English sparrow**, meadowlark, scarlet tanager, song sparrow.

Data relating to mammals and toads are fragmentary compared to those of birds and cannot be taken as so good an indication of the extent to which termites are preyed upon by these groups.

Termites have been found in the stomachs of the black bear, the common mole, the northern hooded skunk, the armadillo, and the white-throated wood rat, in southwestern United States. Three species of toads are known to prey upon termites; their scientific names follow with numbers in parentheses indicating the largest number of termites found in one stomach: *Bufo cognatus* (188), *Bufo compactilis* (2,988), *Bufo punctatus* (290).

In the tropics, in the stomachs of toads *Bufo* spp., of lizards, of birds, and of certain mammals, especially the American anteaters, will often be found rare termites, if the stomachs are examined soon after these reptiles, batrachians, mammals, and birds are killed; otherwise they will be too much digested. Diurnal (day) and nocturnal (night) flying termites as well as workers and soldiers are often present in large numbers.

Some wasps (species of *Polybia*), in South and Middle America kill and decapitate termites — especially species of the sol-

FIG. 48. Remains of headless termites, of the family Termitidae, were found inside of this wasp nest on frond of Cuban Royal palm, *Roystonea regia*, Ancon, Canal Zone, August 11, 1933. The nest is 4 inches in length and 3 inches in width and was made by the wasp *Polybia occidentalis* variety *albopicta* Smith. *Photographed by J. Zetek.*

dierless *Anoplotermes* — and store their bodies in their nests as food (fig. 48). The wasps capture the termites when they are swarming.

Nature has been wise in providing such an enormous number of colonizing adults, because only a small percentage of these potential kings and queens are able to survive such a horde of predators as well as to overcome unfavorable conditions of environment and establish new colonies.

When termites are in their burrows in wood, in the soil, or in carton nests, they are also attacked by animal predators which reduce their numbers. In Chili a small, bluish species of *Peripatus*, a worm-like primitive animal, thought at one time to be the ancestral form of insects, lives in the galleries of a termite in wood; it feeds on the termites. Specially modified spider-like animals or solpugids live in termite nests, where they prey on the inhabitants, as do specialized centipedes. Among the true bugs or sucking insects found with termites are beaked predators (*Triatoma* sp.), as well as peculiar flat, round *Termitaphis*. These latter insects occur in galleries with termites and move about fairly rapidly. Beetle and fly larvae prey on termites in galleries in wood or in their carton nests.

In Africa, the odd-shaped primitive giant pangolin (species of *Manis*), whose body is protected by scales, feeds on termites.

Peculiarly shaped mammals called "anteaters" occur in tropical America. These break into termite nests and devour the inhabitants; they have long claws and a long sticky tongue with which they take up the termites, but they have no teeth. Examination of the stomachs of these animals which have recently fed in the jungle often reveals rare termites and ants and their guests; termites are present in large numbers. The largest of these tropical American anteaters (*Myrmecophaga tridactyla*) (Plate IX, fig. A) has a bushy tail, and when the animal walks the long claws are folded under the foot. This animal, terrestrial in habit, is very wild in the forest, and will attack with its long claws when efforts are made towards its capture. When removed from its forest haunts it soon becomes tame and can be picked up and carried under one's arm. Such animals may be seen alive in the Zoo at Washington, D. C. A smaller kind, the arboreal anteater (*Tamandua tetradactyla*) (Plate IX, fig. B) is less dangerous to capture and makes an interesting pet that can be handled with impunity. *Cyclopes didactylus* is another but smaller arboreal anteater (Plate IX, fig. C). This mammal feeds on true ants more than on termites.

Other odd mammals which feed on termites occur in various parts of the tropics, especially in Australia. A peculiar case is the "Aard-wolves" (*Proteles cristatus*) of South Africa which search at night for termites, which are their principal nourishment.

PLATE IX. Three tropical American anteaters.
  A. The terrestrial *Myrmecophaga tridactyla*.
  B. The arboreal *Tamandua tetradactyla*.
  C. The arboreal *Cyclopes didactyla*.

Mammals, such as black bears, skunks, moles, etc., feed on termites, as well as on other insects. Even the primates, or those ape-like mammals most nearly related to man, feed on termites, as well as other insects, in Africa. Some savages eat termites, especially the winged forms, either raw or cooked, and have many devices by which to trap large numbers of the winged adults, at the time of the swarm. The huge queens — often several inches long — are considered a special delicacy and are especially relished. Termite queens, when eaten, also are reputed to have properties that will invigorate old men. Think of the low forms of plant and animal life occurring in the intestines of the termites which are eaten with these insects!

In South Africa, incidentally, after some of these feasts on enormous numbers of termites, the feasters have become ill and deaths have occurred. It is interesting to speculate whether some of the amoebae and spirochaetes found living in the intestines of termites and some of which apparently are closely related to forms pathogenic in man would be injurious to man if ingested with uncooked termites.

Civilized man, of course, by his disturbance of the balance of nature by felling the forests and cultivating the fields, is the most serious enemy of termites! He destroys the original homes of the termites, forcing them to alter their habitats and to invade his own structures and his crops and other works.

CHAPTER X

ARTIFICIAL CONTROL OF TERMITES

THERE is much popular confusion and misunderstanding with regard to our native termites or "white ants" which damage the woodwork of buildings in temperate countries, such as the United States, as well as in the tropics. Householders often find it difficult to distinguish between injury by termites and ants and damage to woodwork caused by "dry rot" or wood-destroying fungi. They also cannot realize that it is not the winged termite adult that does the damage but the wingless worker hidden in the wood, and that they are both the same species.

My purpose is to give an accurate, plainly understandable but also interesting account of the life habits of termites, their damage, and methods of control based on a knowledge of their biology. It is desired to counteract the incorrect and exaggerated accounts, not only of termites but also of the damage they do and of methods of control.

Recently in the vicinity of New York City, and earlier in other localities, the normal spring appearance of winged forms of termites in or about buildings was used by unscrupulous agents to sell useless materials or perform expensive and ineffective treatments to buildings. Salesmen have been exaggerating the danger from termites in an effort to sell treatments, many of which have little or no merit, but which they picture as absolutely necessary to prevent the collapse within a short time of buildings invaded or under alleged danger of being invaded by termites.

Home owners should be aware of overdrawn and alarming reports of injury to buildings by termites. In particular they should be wary when exaggerated statements of this kind form a part of the "sales talk" for a termite treatment. Reports to the federal Bureau of Entomology indicate that some termite-control operators, overemphasizing the real injury that termites are likely to do, are obtaining from home owners hundreds of thousands of dollars and rendering little or no effective service in return.

" Rackets ", or exploitation of the public by the unscrupulous, are today believed by many to be the result of the recent enforcement of liquor prohibition in the United States. Large sums of money received from " bootlegging" liquor enabled vicious and ignorant members of the population to obtain power and control local governments or at least render them impotent. Rackets, however, are not new, as has been discovered by students of ancient Egypt.

Even termite rackets have existed in the past. As early as 1876, Hagen tells an amusing incident of how the known capability for destructiveness of termites was used by rogues to cover thievery. A very large property stored by the French Government in Île de France (Mauritius) was reported to have been destroyed by termites. The home ministers sent to the colonial officers a box containing files, with strict orders to capture each termite, place it in a vise, and file off the teeth — or resign the post.

So today, when a salesman uses the argument: " Use our material or your house will collapse due to the ravages of termites," give pause! Overstressing by high-pressure salesmen should always be a warning danger signal to the purchaser.

Official records indicate that the collapse of a building in continental United States on account of termite damage is so rare as to be for practical purposes a negligible risk. It is true, however, that where termites have been in buildings for many years — as indicated by emerging swarms of the winged forms — the foundation timbers, and even the floors and adjacent woodwork, may have become so weakened as to make necessary some replacement.

An experience of forty years in termite control by federal entomologists indicates that radical reconstruction of the foundations is the only permanent and effective remedy for buildings which, usually because of original faulty construction, have become heavily infested. Such remedial measures as spraying or fumigation, or even removal of the worst infested timbers, without other protection, are at best temporary. Spraying and fumigation are practically useless in the control of subterranean termites.

One of the popular remedies being exploited is the spraying of woodwork with poisons. Spraying of construction timbers or other woodwork, even after boring the timbers and under a forced stream, or under pressure, is of no real value. The poison has little if any penetration unless the timbers are so badly eaten and rotted that they soak up the mixture like a sponge — in which case they are useless and should be replaced.

Another exploited remedy is the poisoning of soil near the foundation walls or supporting pillars underneath the buildings. All that can be said now of such treatment is that it is still very much in the experimental stage: large scale tests by federal entomologists are under way on Long Island, N. Y., at the present time. On present information it cannot be recommended as a permanent remedy.

The essentials of termite-proofing new structures and of remedying termite damage to buildings already constructed are outlined in the following pages. In their own interest, house owners are cautioned not to accept for the control or elimination of termites any new or easy methods, such as fumigation or sprays, spraying of woodwork in place, or soil poisoning. Full details on methods of remedying damage by termites to various types of buildings are to be found in the Appendix. These specifications were written for use by the federal government: i.e., the Treasury Department, and the Home Owners' Loan Corporation, Reconditioning Division. There is also appended a sample tally sheet or typical form for use by inspectors in recording termite damage to buildings. Specifications for the construction of termite-proof buildings are also outlined in detail in the Appendix. These have been included in the mandatory section of the building codes of some cities.

If a different method of curbing termites were devised and put into effect for every one of the approximately 2000 species of termites of the world, or even for the 56 species native to the United States, there would be many complications and frequent need of much expert consultation. Fortunately, the termites of the world for the practical purpose of suppression by man may be regarded as only three species instead of 2000: namely, the dry-wood or non-subterranean type, the subterranean or ground-nesting termites with diffused nests, and the concentrated nest type. The latter type does not occur in the continental United States, so that in this country we have the much simpler problem of only two species, or rather types, with which to deal.

The first step toward the control of termites is to determine which type of termite is doing the damage, and, if the type is a subterranean termite, whether the termite is a wood destroyer or not. For in the southwestern states there occur termites which do not feed on wood. It may be necessary to consult with a state or federal entomologist to determine the type of termite involved, but this can usually be learned from reading about the insects and their different methods of working.

SUBTERRANEAN TERMITES

PROTECTION OF THE WOODWORK OF BUILDINGS. At the very outset it must be plainly understood that there has been no invasion of the United States by termites and that termite damage is not a local problem that should be hidden to protect real estate values. Most of the damage caused to buildings by subterranean termites is due directly to improper methods of construction. Despite popular opinion, the age of the building does not determine whether or not it is liable to termite attack, since newly constructed buildings are often badly damaged by termites.

Furthermore, it is not the type or kind of construction material, but the manner in which it is utilized in construction, that will lead to or prevent termite damage to buildings. Wood, masonry, concrete, brick, hollow-tile, stucco, and even rammed earth can be effectively used so that the building will not be attacked by termites, if the possibility of termite damage is given careful consideration when the plans are being drawn up by the architect.

Periodic inspections of the premises will greatly reduce the danger of serious damage by termites; and such inspections, together with some of the simpler remedial measures, to be later recommended, may suffice to protect the property.

DESTRUCTION OF BREEDING PLACES ABOUT THE BUILDING SITE. If buildings are to be constructed on recently cleared woodland, decaying logs and stumps and all wood débris should be removed from the soil in the vicinity and burned. If, because of the presence of decaying wood and humus, the subterranean termites are numerous in the earth, the soil should be deeply plowed or otherwise broken up and treated with chemicals to kill the insects. There are several effective poisons for this purpose: a 10% solution of sodium arsenite, which is a dangerous stomach poison and should be used with care (this poison is caustic and should not be used near living vegetation) ; lead arsenate (5 pounds per 1000 square feet of surface) ; one part coal-tar creosote and three parts kerosene oil (this mixture should be strained through burlap before use) ; carbon-disulphide emulsion, which is on the market ready for use; ortho-dichlorobenzene (50 gallons per 1000 square feet). Decaying fence posts, sidewalks, etc., should be removed and replaced with treated wood, concrete, stone, or other resistant substances; such decaying material would facilitate the formation or perpetuation of the termite colonies.

PROPER CONSTRUCTION OF BUILDINGS. Termites will infest not only old buildings but also improperly constructed new buildings, and these are often badly infested. It is not the age of the building but the manner in which it has been constructed that renders it susceptible to attack.

TYPES OF CONSTRUCTION AGAINST TERMITES. It would seem obvious that the first consideration of the prospective home owner and builder should be the adoption of a type of construction which would prevent the entry of termites. That this can be done has been well demonstrated, and it involves only slight additional cost, which may be many times returned in the avoidance of repairs necessitated by the entrance of termites.

To indicate the likelihood of termite invasion under different types of construction, the following list is presented, beginning with the type of building most liable to attack by termites and leading to the most secure:

1. Wooden houses built directly on the ground or supported on wooden posts.

2. Houses built on, or supported by, hollow masonry units uncapped and without concrete footings.

3. Wooden houses built on masonry pillars or with continuous masonry underpinning but without full protection over unexcavated earth.

4. Buildings, frame or stone, with concrete base throughout

but with joists and basement floors laid directly in wet concrete, or with connecting terraces, sun parlors, porches, steps, etc., filled in with earth and wood débris.

5. Buildings in which the foundation or basement construction is of close-grained heartwood termite-resistant woods, such as California redwood, southern cypress, and longleaf pine, and further protected by metal shields.

6. Houses in which all wood used in foundation or basement construction has been impregnated with an approved preservative and further protected with metal shields.

7. Houses the foundation or basements of which are entirely concrete, including baseboards, with cove or "sanitary arc".

BUILDING TERMITE-PROOF. On the basis of the classification just given, it is obvious that where such course is possible, all wood should be eliminated from foundations, cellars, and basements, including porches, sun parlors, etc., with the substitution therefor of masonry or concrete, and this should apply both to houses of masonry construction and those having a wood superstructure.

This type of construction insures the fullest protection from termite entry, and has been given first importance by the Bureau of Entomology for twenty-five to thirty years.

BUILDING FOR REASONABLE SECURITY. Where, for economy or because there is less need for durability, it is desirable to use wood as supporting posts or as joists or beams, etc., in the foundations and basements of buildings, the risk from termites can be prevented — if not fully, at least for many years — by strict observance of the following recommendations:

1. All structural wood to be so employed in or within 18 inches of the earth should be treated as indicated in the following paragraph with a preservative which will repel termites. Such treatment need not be given to wood columns and posts resting on a concrete floor, but additional security can be provided by placing them on noncorroding metal plates or on concrete footings rising somewhat above the floor level. Wooden door casings in such basement rooms will be given added security if the lower 5 or 6 inches of the casings are in the form of a properly shaped concrete block rising from and continuous with the floor. The door itself needs no protection. Further, it is not necessary to use treated wood for steps built over a

concrete base if the concrete is given a projection of at least 6 inches beyond the steps. The additional security of footings of the nature indicated is especially called for in the more southern portions of the United States.

2. All timber to be used in contact with or near the earth should be thoroughly impregnated by a standard pressure proc-ess with coal-tar creosote or an equivalent preservative. When-ever possible timber should be cut to proper dimensions before

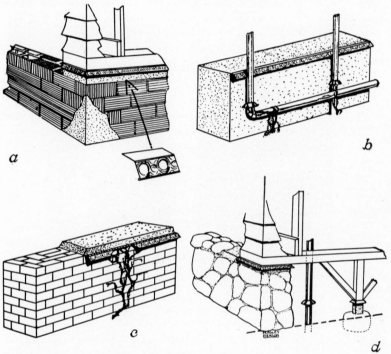

FIG. 49. How to insulate foundation units of hollow tile or solid masonry against termites.

a. Foundation wall of hollow tile surfaced with stucco, showing metal ter-mite shield in place. Notice how the top of the wall is capped with sheet slate and concrete.

b. Concrete wall with termite shield at top, the horizontally laid piping fitted above bend with metal shield to shut off termite tubes. The vertical pipe also has a termite shield.

c. Brick wall fitted with termite shield and capped with concrete. Notice how the shield mechanically blocks the earth-like shelter tubes of the termites.

d. Stone wall fitted with termite shield and capped with concrete, the wooden posts insulated from the ground with base stone and concrete block. Notice the termite shields on the post and piping.

treatment, but when cutting after treatment is unavoidable the cut surface should be thoroughly coated with the preservative. Concerns equipped to give such treatment are available in different parts of the United States, and the security of treated material should be required in the building specifications.

3. Masonry foundations and footings preferably should be laid in Portland-cement mortar and with all joinings well filled and pointed. Foundations built of artificial masonry units whether hollow or solid should be capped below the woodwork

FIG. 50. View of a metal termite shield on the foundation of a building in the Canal Zone, Panama.

with at least one inch of Portland-cement mortar, or with mortar and slate, or with solid or joined noncorroding metal.

4. As protection against entry into houses through shelter tubes — and this applies particularly to southern areas — metal shields should be provided around the top of the masonry foundation (figs. 49 and 50), and around all pillars, supports (fig. 49), and piping (fig. 51), below the woodwork of frame buildings. Such protection should also be given to all inside surfaces which can be reached by termites from unprotected soil. The shields may be formed of a strip of noncorroding metal (such as copper, or zinc, or an alloy composed of 28 per cent copper,

67 per cent nickel, and 5 per cent iron, manganese, and silicon) firmly inserted in the surface of the masonry, or between the foundation and the wood, with the projecting edge bent downward at an angle of 45 degrees, and extending horizontally at least 2 inches from the face of the foundation.[1]   The metal should be over 1/32 of an inch in thickness.   In masonry buildings this shield should be inset in the masonry at a height at least 18 inches above the ground (fig. 49).   Care should be taken that this metal strip should not have objects rested against it so as to bend it out of shape.

Fig. 51.   A view of metal termite shields in place about piping under a frame building at Honolulu, Hawaii.   *Photo. by Ehrhorn.*

5. Where only a portion of the space under the house is to be excavated for cellar or basement rooms, the balance, including the space under sun parlors, porches, etc., should be excavated so that there will be no earth within 18 inches of the wood, and this area should also be provided with cross ventilation.   Such ventilating openings should be proportioned on the basis of 2 square feet for each 25 linear feet of exterior wall, except that such openings need not be placed in the front of the building. Each opening should be provided with 20-mesh noncorroding-metal screening, including windows in attics.

Hence it will be seen that proper construction is a form of insurance against termite injury.   Furthermore, practically all

---

[1] The cost of 16 ounce sheet hard copper is approximately 15 cents per linear foot, including price of bending and installation.

such injury to the woodwork of buildings can be prevented and remedied by proper construction based on a knowledge of the habits of termites.

CITY BUILDING CODES. Urban communities can do much to prevent termite damage by including in their building regulations or codes a few simple provisions which, if enforced, will protect houses from termites. Some cities now have such rules governing the construction of buildings and they have proven to be very helpful. Realizing that proper construction is fun-

FIG. 52. Lumber raised off the ground on concrete piers. Inset shows how metal termite shields should have been placed over these piers to stop the earth-like shelter tubes of subterranean termites.

damental, since 1923 the federal Bureau of Entomology has urged the inclusion in mandatory city building codes of a few simple provisions as the logical solution of the problem. These practical and brief suggestions when enforced will not only prevent damage by termites but can also be used in remedying damage to buildings already infested by termites. The Bureau of Entomology will gladly supply information that will aid in drafting suitable regulations.

Essentially they pertain to methods of keeping termites from coming up from the ground, where they live and obtain moisture, and burrowing into the untreated woodwork of buildings. In other words, they are intended to secure the insulation of untreated wood from contact with the ground.

These provisions for the protection of householders against careless construction often mean but slight modification of ex· isting building codes.

COST OF TERMITE-PROOFING. A few hundred dollars additional spent in the proper construction of buildings may save thousands of dollars later in repairs and replacements. It is much simpler and cheaper to keep termites out of a building than to get rid of them and repair the damage after they are once in. These suggestions for the prevention of termite damage to buildings will probably add only from 1 to 2 per cent to the initial cost of the buildings (mainly chargeable to supervision) but they are a form of insurance, not only to the householder, but to the person financing the buildings. Bankers have shown their understanding of this point by their willingness to lend more money or give a lower rate of interest to a home owner constructing a building in accordance with these provisions.

In rural regions, county agricultural representatives are available for assistance and advice to prospective housebuilders and owners on the proper methods of construction so necessary to prevent termite damage.

In recent years some progress has been made. I attended in 1927 the annual meeting of the Pacific Coast Building Officials Conference held at Phoenix, Arizona. This conference adopted the suggestions made by the Bureau of Entomology for the inclusion of brief provisions in city building codes to prevent termite damage. On pages 214 and 215 of their Uniform Building Code, 1927 edition, you will find these suggestions. Unfortunately, these provisions are in the appendix and not under the mandatory sections of the code.

A few cities in California, Hawaii, the southern states, and other scattered sections of this country have included in building codes brief protective provisions against termites. There has been, however, no definite campaign to so protect the public. Architects, engineers, and contractors by close cooperation soon could convince life insurance and building and loan associations that proper construction would protect their investments.

As I was told when, in 1927, I addressed a group of Japanese
contractors — who do most of the construction work in Honolulu — first you must convince the public by educational propa-
ganda that the slightly increased costs are a form of insurance
against termite attack.   Incidentally, in Honolulu, even the
newsboys on the streets are termite-conscious.   Concerted effort
by all concerned is necessary, and even after protective provisions have been included in city building codes they must be
enforced!

Several states have made independent investigations of termites and have endeavored to protect their citizens from losses
caused by termites.   The State of California has taken aggressive
action and instituted important measures to protect the homes
and other structures of its citizens from damage by termites.

In August, 1928, the Termite Investigations Committee was
formed with an advisory council composed of technical men on
the faculty of the University of California, including Dr. S. F.
Light, an international authority on termites, and headed by
Dr. C. A. Kofoid.   It was to be a cooperative research effort on
the part of various industries of the State of California, seeking
a full understanding of the economic problems raised by the
attacks of termites on wooden structures and some practical solution therefor.   The final report of this committee, which I
served in an advisory capacity, was published in January, 1934.

Another protective move is the requirement by the State of
California (Sec. 2322 of the Political Code) that certificates be
required for commercial operators to treat properties for termites; this offers assurance to householders that the operators
have passed an examination showing their ability.   Such regulations for the certification of pest-control operators should be
enforced in all states, and if nation-wide in scope would at least
ensure that the operators have the necessary knowledge.

AN UNWELCOME DISCOVERY.   Many people have had sad ex-
periences with termites damaging their homes, which had been
purchased without careful examination to determine whether
or not the building had been properly constructed.   Each case of
damage to small houses or large public buildings presents different features; but an actual, average case is as follows:

A young married couple, living on a salary, have recently purchased a new home on the installment plan and are very proud

of their place.   One spring morning a year later, the wife dis-
covers a large number of " flying ants " in the building.   Investi-
gation shows that the insects had entered through untreated
woodwork in contact with the ground (which is the chief source
of infestation) but that they had also entered through poor
grades of mortar between masonry in the foundations, and had
worked up through the interior of walls.   Also, by means of
earth-like shelter tubes or covered runways built over impenetrable masonry foundations, the termites had reached the woodwork above.

Repairs to shut off the subterranean termites from the earth,

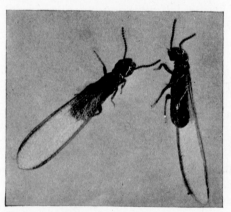

Fig. 53.   Winged adults of our native southern subterranean termite (*Reticulitermes
virginicus* Banks).   Enlarged about six
times.

where they obtain the moisture so necessary to their life, are
estimated to cost over five hundred dollars.   The house had been
purchased on the installment plan by the payment of a large
initial sum, and the family is living on a budget.   When the repairs have been made and paid for, the family cannot meet its
notes at the bank.

The banker becomes interested and learns that the damage
was caused by improper construction of the building; in fact,
was due to speculative building.   A consultation with the city
building inspector follows and through the influence of banks,
building and loan associations, and insurance companies, the
city building code is revised to include suggestions for prevent-

ing termite damage to buildings in the "mandatory" section. Thus, the small householder can be protected and those financing the building can have their investment secured — a form of insurance for all concerned.

LOOK OUT FOR "FLYING ANTS". So, when you find small, blackish, white-winged "ants" (see the illustration herewith: fig. 53) flying in large numbers about your house in the spring and fall, do not sweep them up, thinking they are merely out-

FIG. 54. View of winged adults of the southeastern subterranean termite swarming from the woodwork of a building at Washington, D. C.

door ants, and then forget about them. They may be termites, and perhaps are destroying the woodwork of your home.

HOW TO LOCATE DAMAGE. Early indication of the presence of termites may come from the emergence in the buildings in spring and fall of the winged migrating males and females. Incidentally, sweeping up and killing these swarming insects, while a good thing in itself, does not in any way stop the damage, inasmuch as the full strength of the invaders will be maintained from the parent colony until adequate and usually radical measures have been taken to isolate the building and stop further invasion. These winged adults are harmless indoors and will soon die if they cannot burrow into moist earth. When annoying, they can be swept up in a vacuum cleaner.

Another warning that termites are around is the branching shelter tubes on foundation walls reaching from the ground to the woodwork, over the surface of stone, brick, or other foundation material through which the termites cannot burrow (fig. 32).

When the presence of termites has been discovered, the location of the termites and the extent of their work cannot necessarily be determined by the point of emergence of the winged forms, but usually will be indicated by the yielding of basement flooring or the softening or yielding of wainscoting, studding, etc., or by evidences of their destructive work in books, etc.

How to Stop Termite Damage. The means of stopping termite injury in a building are substantially the same as those to be employed in new construction to prevent the entry of termites. Inasmuch as contact with soil moisture is absolutely essential to the life of ground-inhabiting termites, reconstruction of a type which permanently breaks and makes impassable the ground connections maintained between the parent soil colony and any building will result in the prompt dying of any termites remaining in the woodwork or furniture or contents of the building even if they have reached the second or third floor. However, if through water leakage or other source such woodwork is kept more or less permanently moist, termites cut off in the building may continue to work as long as this condition lasts, and this applies particularly to damp corners of basements or similar conditions which may result from leakages of waterpipes in bathrooms, kitchens, etc.

The Two Best Remedies. The most lasting and effective remedy, as already indicated, is the replacement of wood in or near the basement of the building with concrete (fig. 55). Second in order of effectiveness and durability is replacement of such wood with treated wood or timbers, and, in regions of excessive termite damage, to employ under both methods protective shields. By this means contact between colony and building is permanently broken and relief from termite damage is assured. This means that joists imbedded in concrete and the basement floor and baseboards should be replaced with any type of plain or ornamental concrete. In basement rooms so constructed, movable furniture of wood, and also built-in furniture, particularly if resting on concrete footings, can be employed with safety.

CAPPING AND FACING. To give the capping and facing to base-

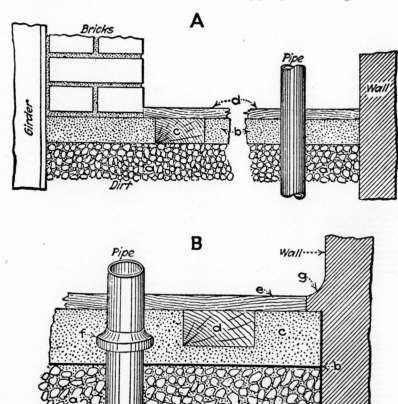

FIG. 55. A. Improperly constructed concrete flooring: (a) gravel or cinders loosely cemented with coarse concrete, 3 inches thick, but with many crevices and holes; (b) solid, dense concrete, 2 inches thick; (c) untreated wood sleeper set in moist concrete over the grout; (d) flooring nailed to sleepers. B. Properly constructed concrete flooring: (a) gravel or cinders loosely cemented with coarse concrete, but with many crevices and holes; (b) coal tar pitch waterproofing ⅛ inch thick; (c) dense concrete, 3 inches thick; (d) treated wood sleeper set in a groove in concrete which insulates it from termites in the earth; (e) flooring nailed on sleepers; (f) metal collar around pipe which runs down through the concrete (this collar should be soldered to the pipe and embedded in the concrete); (g) shoulder of concrete at joint of wall and concrete floor to avoid a right-angle connection and consequent cracking.

ment walls of frame buildings, it is rarely necessary to jack up the building, but usually it is possible to remove the upper tier of brick or upper portion of the masonry unit in sections and replace with Portland-cement mortar and suitable capping of slate or mortar.

Where poor grades of mortar have been used in masonry walls below the ground, it may be necessary to coat the outside, and perhaps also the inside, of the wall with Portland cement or neat concrete to keep termites from boring through.

METAL TERMITE SHIELDS. The termite shields of metal can easily be inserted over or in the masonry foundation of buildings or around pillars, supports, piping, etc., below the frame superstructure.

SOIL POISONS. The possibility of stopping, for a temporary period at least, termite work in buildings by means of soil poisons placed about the foundations is indicated by experiments which have been under way for several years. The use of such soil poisons is, however, still very much in the experimental stage and on present information cannot be recommended as a permanent remedy. On the other hand, where termite reconstruction herein recommended is deemed by the owner to be impracticable or too expensive, the following type of soil poisoning may be used and should give temporary relief.

The most promising of the soil poisons for such use is full strength crude liquid orthodichlorobenzene. This chemical should be applied in a trench close to the exterior foundation walls and also along the interior of such walls or piers in all unexcavated areas under the building. Dig a trench 18 to 30 inches deep (in no case lower than the top of footing) around the foundation walls, removing all wood débris and breaking off all earth-like shelter tubes over foundations. Saturate the soil at the bottom of the trench with full strength orthodichlorobenzene at the rate of one gallon per ten linear feet; then replace the soil and repeat the treatment within 3 inches of the surface. Similarly orthodichlorobenzene should be applied about masonry pillars supporting the main structure or porches, etc. This liquid can be obtained at a reasonable price from wholesale chemists or manufacturers of insecticides.

The cautions to be observed in the use of this chemical are not to let it come in contact with the face and hands, as it burns slightly, and is distinctly painful if it gets into the eyes. In applying it to a closed space beneath the building, the operator should not remain too long subject to the fumes, and it is desirable to secure as good ventilation as possible while applying the chemical.

In cases where there is danger of orthodichlorobenzene reaching the spreading roots of living vegetation, use paradichlorobenzene in the crystalline form in the same manner as specified above. Crystals should be used at the rate of approximately five pounds per ten linear feet. Or use a mixture of one part coal tar creosote and three parts kerosene oil at the rate of one gallon of this mixture per ten linear feet.

The use of these and other soil poisons is especially applicable to buildings raised on masonry pillars or partially filled-in basements or porches, but, as already indicated, such treatments lack adequate proof of effectiveness and permanency.

CAUTION AGAINST EXAGGERATED FEARS. Without desire to minimize the damage which may be occasioned to buildings and contents from termite attack, especially if long continued, it should nevertheless be pointed out that, particularly in the more temperate zones, serious termite injury to buildings is relatively infrequent and termite work may go on for years without involving the necessity for extensive repairs or reconstruction of foundation timbers and flooring. Many instances could be cited of old houses dating back to colonial times where termite presence has been known for fifty years and probably two or three times that period without radical injury resulting. Such immunity is due, in part, to the more massive timbers employed in these older types of houses, the foundation beams of which were often of large size and hewn from the mature centers of hardwood trees.

Once having invaded a building, however, termites will continue their work and extend their damage slowly or rapidly unless and until means of entrance from the outside has been broken by effective reconstruction. With the breaking of the connection between the building and the external soil moisture, all the termites in the building promptly die and injury ceases.

On March 20, 1934, a heavy beam from one of the temporary government buildings which had been badly damaged by the southern subterranean termite was removed from ground connection and taken into a steam-heated building. Within a few days it became evident that there was not sufficient moisture within the wood to sustain the termites, since they came out of the wood and fell to the floor in a shrivelled condition. On March 26 a great many of the workers were dead and shrivelled, but winged adults continued to swarm from the wood, still being apparently in normal condition. On March 28 the winged adults were able to crawl from the wood but could not fly. On March 29, all of the castes were either moribund or dead.

Although the danger of sudden collapse of any fairly well constructed building strictly from termite injury can be dismissed as very slight in the United States, the presence of termites in a building, indicated either by swarming or by the yielding of flooring and timbers, certainly calls for an examination to determine what means should be taken to stop damage. If on such examination fairly widespread injury is found, much the cheapest course in the long run is to undertake one or the other of the two types of radical replacement given the highest rating in this book. The natural tendency of the home owner is, however, to attempt control by local applications or other simple measures.

Due to the extent of the possible ramifications of termites in a building which has been infested for some little time and the protection which they have in their burrows concealed in the wood, no control worth while by fumigation or spraying has proved to be possible, and spraying, even if applied under strong pressure at borings made at occasional points in eaten timbers, is unsatisfactory. It is of interest, therefore, and informing, to point out that in the case of many prominent buildings, both federal and residential, in Washington, after years of effort with the various possible methods of local application of correctives, repellents, etc., together with piecemeal replacement of eaten timbers, the more radical type of correction here recommended has finally been adopted, and has resulted in prompt and complete elimination of termites.

NOT ALL TERMITES ARE WOOD DESTROYERS. In connection with the foregoing discussion, it is well to point out that in certain areas, particularly in the southwestern states, there occur types of termites which never feed upon or bore into — nor in fact can they digest — sound wood, and hence never attack wood in buildings or elsewhere. These types feed on low vegetation, grasses, etc.: they cover the stems with earth-like tubes, and the resulting partially decayed vegetable material is the only food on which they can subsist. The presence of the earth-like tubes of these termites near or even under houses, or the presence of the winged forms may be wrongly interpreted as indicating likelihood of invasion by one of the wood-eating termites; and therefore the house owner should make sure that any agency professing to give termite control is able to distinguish between this form and the destructive type of termites. Before authorizing control measures involving what may prove to be quite unnecessary outlays, the owner, if in doubt, should consult his state entomologist or send specimens for identification to the United States Bureau of Entomology, Washington, D. C.

<h3 style="text-align:center">DRY–WOOD TERMITES</h3>

In regions such as the tropics and subtropics, where much damage is caused by dry-wood termites, all doors, windows, or other ventilation openings in buildings should be properly screened with 20-mesh, noncorroding metal screening, especially in the case of attics. This will prevent the entrance of the winged termites, which bore directly into wood.

Foundation timbers should be impregnated with coal tar creosote. Interior woodwork should be given at least brush or dipping treatments with zinc chloride or other equivalent preservatives and then painted with a heavy enamel paint. Such thick paints alone will afford some protection from attack by this type of termite, and paint also should be applied to woodwork in attics, as well as elsewhere where it is not ordinarily painted because not visible. To afford permanent protection to buildings, all woodwork used in buildings should be impregnated with standard chemical wood preservatives, especially in regions where there is considerable damage by dry-wood termites. Such treatment is recommended to persons who can afford this additional expense. Such use of impregnated wood would increase the initial cost of termite proofing to approximately ten per cent of the cost of building. This would cover the additional cost of handling treated timber.

This impregnation should be made before the wood is placed in the structure and should be given to wood cut to exact neces-

sary dimensions. In case the impregnated wood is to be framed·
after treating, the cut surfaces should be given a brush or dipping
treatment with the hot chemical. Such impregnated wood or
timber can be purchased from wood-preserving companies in
various sections of the United States.

For interior woodwork and furniture, which require subsequent finish, such as waxing, varnishing or painting, an impregnation giving an average absorption of ¾ to 1½ pounds of dry
zinc chloride salt per cubic foot is recommended. Sodium flu-
oride and chlorinated naphthalene and other equivalent preservatives, while more expensive, are effective preservatives for
timber not to be used in contact with the ground, where moisture would cause leaching out in the case of soluble salts.

Wood-pulp or fiber products, such as the various wood-fiber
processed or composition boards, or cane-fiber boards, for interior finish and substitute for lath, or for exterior use, can be
protected from attack by termites by adding certain poisons to
the pulp or laminated boards in the course of manufacture.
Several suitable poisons, such as coal tar creosote (at the rate of
two gallons per thousand square feet), have been found effective
and practical. Further experiments in testing additional chemicals suitable for this type of product are under way. In the case
of insulating boards care should be taken that neither the poison
nor the method of applying it interferes with the insulating qual-
ities of the board.

There should be large wholesale and retail markets, not only
in this country but especially in the tropics of the world where
termites are extremely injurious, for timber, lumber, and furniture which have been impregnated with standard wood preservatives, not only to protect wood against termites, but also against
decay and fire. Impregnation extends the uses of wood for purposes where in an untreated condition it would not be satisfactory. Initial greater cost is warranted by the long-time insurance against loss.

The greater use of timber and lumber impregnated with
standard chemical wood preservatives will not only protect the
user from loss through damage by insects and decay but is also
important in the conservation of our forest resources, because
of the increased length of service which is assured wood so
treated.

In most parts of continental United States the use of impregnated timber throughout the building is unnecessary, for as we have already shown damage by dry-wood termites is uncommon, local and slight, often being more apparent than real structural weakening. The marred surface of the wood, where the thin outer shell left by the insects becomes broken in, and the dropping of pellets of excrement from infested wood become a nuisance.

Where there is any danger to human beings, weakened wood must be removed and replaced with impregnated timber, or the subterranean termites killed by shutting them off from the ground; or, if they are dry-wood termites, they should be poisoned with dry Paris green blown into their galleries, and then the timbers if in the roof should be reinforced by structural steel. A building inspector can take no chances! Halfway measures may cause loss of life. Paris green has been proved effective in Hawaii, Panama, Ceylon, and the United States. Biology can explain why: termites constantly lick each other and themselves and become poisoned on these powders.

Buildings are sometimes infested with both subterranean and non-subterranean termites; rot may also be present to further complicate the problem.

In 1922, at the request of the owners, I inspected a large frame hotel on one of the islands in the Bahamas. The woodwork and the furniture of the large frame structure were thoroughly infested with a powder-post termite (*Cryptotermes brevis* Walker). In addition the foundations had been attacked by tropical subterranean termites (species of *Heterotermes* and *Nasutitermes*). It was fairly easy to remedy the damage by these subterranean termites and to prevent further attack, but the powder-post termites were so intrenched that, while the use of poisons was recommended, it was felt that the real remedy would be to tear down the building and burn all of the material. As a matter of fact, the hotel did accidentally burn down not long after, thereby eliminating a huge source of infestation. If the building had been torn down the infested wood would have been resold and this would have resulted in new centers of infestation where next used.

The officials of the Panama Canal prohibit the transportation of such infested wood from one part of the Zone to another. Re-

cently the State of Florida ruled likewise in the case of the woodwork of a large hotel at Miami which was infested by *Cryptotermes brevis* Walker. The infested wood was put on sale but
was ordered burned by the state officials. Unfortunately the
similarly infested furniture had already been sold, and every so
often the U. S. Bureau of Entomology is called upon by those
who bought the " worm-eaten " furniture for advice as to how
to remedy the infestation.

In Cuba, Havana and most other large municipalities have
building ordinances which prohibit the use of wooden floors;
Havana is very strict in regulating against the use of wood for
the construction of permanent buildings. Damage by powder-
post or house termites to the woodwork of buildings and furniture has been very marked in the past. Use of wood for the
construction of buildings is, in fact, limited to the rural regions.
Termite-resistant wood is favored in Cuba. Such woods as Spanish cedar (*Cedrella*), pitch pine, heartwood redwood, and heartwood cypress are commonly used.

Fumigation, poisons, and spraying of infested woodwork are
of no permanent value against subterranean termites in buildings, for although they may kill the flying insects and some others
in the wood, more will continue to come up from the ground.
However, these methods are of some use against dry-wood termites.

In the case of termites which do not live in the ground, however, but attack wood directly, it is advisable to remove and replace the wood if the damage is slight and localized. Where the
wood has been seriously damaged, but not structurally weakened, saturate the infested wood with orthodichlorobenzene.
The infested wood should be thoroughly saturated with this
chemical: a rag or mop should be used, dripping wet, or the
liquid can be applied as a spray. Several applications may be
necessary to kill the insects, and after drenching the wood a careful watch should be maintained until it is certain that all the
termites are dead.

If orthodichlorobenzene is used as a spray, it is advised that
the house be opened up before and for some time after treatment, since there is quite an odor to the chemical which may
prove disagreeable in a closed room. Also, in spraying timbers
overhead, care should be taken not to let the liquid drip down,

PLATE X. Heat chambers, such as the one at Honolulu, Hawaii pictured above, should be constructed at all sea-ports where dry-wood termites or other wood-borers are apt to be introduced.

A. A passenger car ready to be brought from the heat chamber, the iron work on the car being so hot that it cannot be held.

B. The side of the chamber, which is 75 feet long, showing the location of the thermograph on the exterior.

C. The door of the chamber and the locomotive from which heat is furnished by means of live steam through pipes at 90 pounds pressure.

since it might slightly burn the face and hands and would be painful if it got in the eyes.

If the orthodichlorobenzene treatment is not practicable and the wood is too thick for the solution to penetrate, blow dry Paris green or the safer, less poisonous sodium fluosilicate (which, however, is not as effective) by means of a bellows into holes bored with an auger into the infested wood; these holes should penetrate to the galleries of the termites. If, because of moisture, the Paris green becomes caked, the treatment should be repeated. When the termites groom or lick themselves after becoming covered with the poisonous dusts they take the poison into their systems.

Furniture infested by termites of this type is usually fumigated in steel cylinders with carbon disulphide gas, or given the more effective heat treatments.

Heat has been effectively utilized in killing termites infesting the woodwork of railroad cars, furniture, etc. In Hawaii, a chamber of reinforced concrete, large enough to contain a passenger coach or two freight cars run in on rails, was specially constructed. The sides of the interior of the chamber were equipped with coils of piping in which live steam from a locomotive was utilized, and at 90 pounds pressure it was possible to subject the infested wood to temperatures of 150 degrees F., maintained for at least one and one-half hours. The heat was applied and gradually raised; the temperature could be determined from a thermograph on the exterior of the building. The paint or varnish finish on the wood of the cars treated was not injured by the heat (Plate X).

Such a chamber should be located at all ports where wood infested by dry-wood termites or other borers is likely to be brought in, and the infested wood subjected to a heat treatment, which is more reliable than fumigation.

PROTECTION OF TELEPHONE, TELEGRAPH, ELECTRIC LIGHT, RADIO, AND OTHER POLES

SUPERFICIAL PRESERVATIVE TREATMENTS. Impregnation with standard grades of coal tar creosote is the most effective and practicable method of wood preservation for poles where long service is to be required. Such treatment is costly, but thoroughly protects poles from attacks by termites and other wood-boring insects and from decay.

Such superficial methods of application as brushing or dipping poles with or in coal tar creosote are only temporarily effective, but will add length of service to poles. In commercial enterprises, the type of treatment must necessarily be determined by cost, amount of loss due to termites, and length of service to be expected.

Where the poles are damaged after being put in place, as in the case of lumber, the cost of replacement involves additional loss of labor and time, as well as the cost of the original and replaced poles, a loss far greater than the value of the raw product. Sometimes such replacement charges should be attributed to both wood-destroying fungi and termites and not to one agency alone, as frequently there is a close relationship between these forms of life in the destruction of timber. However, in many cases wood-destroying fungi or termites alone are responsible for the destruction.

When brush treatments are used, only high-grade antiseptic preservatives such as standard grades of coal tar creosote oils or carbolineums should be employed, since the cost of application of brush treatments is often high. The cost of any treatment should necessarily be more than offset by the longer service assured by the application. The several methods of application or impregnation of the preservative should be determined by the length of service required and the consequent expenditure warranted.

Both brushing, dipping and spraying applications of coal tar creosote penetrate the wood but slightly, and permanent protection is not to be expected. Red or green pigments may be added to the oil to give the wood a painted appearance. After such treatments the poles often season check and these crevices afford entrance to both insects and decay. Often such superficial treatments are not thoroughly applied and not all areas and crevices are treated.

IMPREGNATION PRESERVATIVE TREATMENTS

OPEN TANK. Impregnation of the butts of poles with coal tar creosote by the open tank method will effectively protect poles from attack by the subterranean types of termites and from decay near the ground line, where the greatest structural strength is required in poles. The open tank method can be utilized in treating poles with makeshift or homemade equipment, and unskilled labor can be employed.

In the case of improperly seasoned butt-treated poles or in certain climates the wood might open up with season checks which extend deeply into the pole beyond or below the outer treated area. The penetration attained by this impregnation process is not always great and cannot compare with that obtained by using a pressure process.

PRESSURE PROCESS. On the average for the United States as a whole, impregnation of the pole (pine) for its entire length by the "full cell" (at least 12 lbs. per cu. ft.) pressure process in large steel cylinders with coal tar creosote of standard grades renders the wood resistant to attack by both types of termites for at least 30 years. There are sections of the country where a percentage of well-treated individual pine poles will be attacked by termites in appreciably less than 30 years, the

FIG. 56. Damage to yellow pine telephone pole impregnated with twelve pounds of coal tar creosote per cubic foot, attacked by subterranean termites after about 15 years of service in Mississippi. Outer layers broken away to show damage. Insects entered through deep season checks.

period of sure resistance being lessened by changes in the composition of the creosote resulting from service exposure (fig. 56).

If, as in cities, there is danger of the creosote "bleeding", "sweating" or oozing out in hot weather, poles can be treated by the "empty cell" method, where under a vacuum part of the creosote oil can be withdrawn so that there is no danger of persons soiling their clothing by contact with such wet creosoted poles. Furthermore, poles thus treated are less difficult and disagreeable to handle, and the setting crews do not object to working with them. The use of heavy gloves and a little care should overcome all difficulties in handling creosoted poles.

The use of a pressure process requires special expensive equipment and skilled labor. Most companies utilizing such impregnated poles purchase them: by the use of an increment borer the average penetration of the creosote can be determined. In the case of southern yellow pine with much sapwood a uniform penetration of three inches can be obtained. While Douglas fir of the Pacific Coast has been more difficult to impregnate, a satisfactory penetration to the extent of the sapwood can be attained by incising.

In areas where they are seriously damaged by non-subterranean termites, pine or Douglas fir cross-arms and insulator pegs or pins can also be impregnated with coal tar creosote.

CREOSOTED POLES CAN BE PAINTED. If it is desired — as in cities — to paint poles after impregnation they can be painted with an aluminum paint over the creosote, and the creosote will not show through if the creosoted poles are allowed to dry thoroughly before painting. After this coat the aluminum paint can be repainted, if other colors are desired.

COMBINATION OF THE IMPREGNATION AND SUPERFICIAL PRESERVATIVE TREATMENTS

If after the butts of poles have received an open tank impregnation treatment they are dipped for their entire length in an elongate vat filled with hot coal tar creosote, some protection from attack by dry-wood termites and decay will be afforded to the entire pole. This vat should be wide and deep enough to hold at least 3 or 4 poles at once and the poles should be buried or creosote should be slopped over them with a scoop.

This is in no sense an open tank treatment, but it should offer some protection to the pole; the creosote penetrates season checks and other holes. It is not an expensive treatment compared to full-length impregnation of poles and homemade equipment and unskilled labor can be used. Although still in the experimental stage, the combination process appears promising. Old poles which have been infested by the non-subter-

ranean termites can also be so treated after they have been removed, and their length of service in the line thus prolonged.

PRESERVATIVE TREATMENTS FOR POLES ALREADY SET OR IN PLACE

There must often be an effort made to prolong the length of
service of poles already in place because of the large amount of
capital already invested and the undesirability of the disturbance necessary in replacing operations. Experiments to prolong
the life of standing poles infested with termites have been conducted for some time.

STUMPING. Poles damaged at the base are sometimes braced
by fastening to them an auxiliary stub or stump impregnated
with coal tar creosote.

RESETTING. The butts of damaged poles are cut off and the
portion of the pole to go in the ground is brushed with coal tar
creosote. This, of course, lowers the height of the wires.

CHARRING AND SPRAYING. The butts of poles are charred
with a blow torch and then sprayed with coal tar creosote or
kerosene oil, thus ensuring greater penetration of the oils.

SOIL POISONING. Treating the soil about poles with poisonous liquids or powders may be at least temporarily effective in
remedying and preventing termite damage. Our experiments
to date are not conclusive as to either the most effective chemicals or methods of application. A promising method is to excavate the earth to the depth of 30 inches, then pour the liquids
or powders in trenches about the pole and replace the earth.
Five gallons of liquid per pole, evenly distributed in trenches
every six inches, or five pounds of powder equally distributed
in trenches every ten inches, appear to be practical amounts.

Smaller dosages might be used, but the type of soil must be
considered when specifying the amount of chemical. Three
miles of pole line or 100 poles can be thus treated per day. How
long such poisons will remain effective is not at present known.
Rainfall is undoubtedly an important factor in determining
how long the poisons will last.

Two dollars a year is the maximum amount that can be ex-
pended on such treatments, including inspection. Such en-
deavors in the past have not been very successful and the whole
problem is still in the experimental stage.

HEAT STERILIZATION. Where it is desired to stop the working of dry-wood termites in standing poles which have been removed, or in untreated poles infested before placed in service, they can be subjected to a temperature of 135 to 150 degrees F. with a saturated atmosphere or humidity of 100% in a tight chamber such as a kiln. This temperature maintained for $1\frac{1}{2}$ hours will kill the termites. Such a treatment is not necessary in the case of the subterranean termite, which will dry up and die soon after the pole is removed from the moist soil.

DIFFERENCE IN SOILS. Subterranean termites will not attack poles set in a constantly water-saturated soil or in soils saturated with alkaline salts.

INFESTATION OF POLES BEFORE SERVICE

In the case of a pole yard where old poles infested with non-subterranean termites are stored in order to be salvaged, *no untreated new poles should be stored.* These termites will live more or less indefinitely in the old poles and, when they fly or swarm once each year in late summer or early fall, they will attack the new poles. These poles then will be infested before any service in the line.

It is possible that termites may spread from certain regions more rapidly if untreated pole lines connect their present areas with uninfested regions. It might be possible to remove untreated poles, etc., in which they are now breeding and erect impregnated pole lines, which might serve as barriers. Close observation as to the necessity for such procedure and cooperation with pole companies would be necessary to make such a scheme successful. Termites could then be prevented from crossing deserts and treeless plains to more fertile regions.

PROTECTION OF STORED MATERIAL

It should be clearly understood that any material which contains cellulose is liable to attack by termites. Damage by termites to material stored in buildings is due to the fact that the building itself is infested.

Injury to clothing, books, paper, documents and other stored material is usually indirect, the insects as a rule burrowing through such goods only when they are in contact with infested wood, such as wooden flooring or shelving. Rugs, carpets or linoleum laid over wooden flooring are likely to be damaged by termites coming through the flooring. Books or valuable documents, etc., should not be packed away in warm, unventilated chambers where they become moist and moldy, and, therefore, particularly subject to attack by termites. It should be borne in mind that termites are likely to be present in old buildings, even though their work has not been sufficient to attract attention. Insects infesting stored material soon leave, die out, or can be killed by spreading out the infested books, documents, and other stored material or products to dry in the sun or in an oven, or by putting them outdoors during cold weather. Temperatures over 120 degrees F. will kill the insects.

However, it simplifies the problem when it is realized that repairs to the structure will stop further damage to the contents. Fumigants, sprays, poisons, insecticides, are of no permanent value in preventing or repairing damage to stored materials by subterranean termites. Later, such goods can be restored to the repaired building, since the damage originally was entirely a secondary consequence of the presence of termites.

Damage to stored products by dry-wood termites may be either direct or indirect. Such injury can be stopped by the use of the heat treatment which has already been discussed or by utilizing poison dusts or liquids, as appears most practicable in the individual case.

PREVENTION AND REMEDY OF INJURY TO LIVING VEGETATION

FRUIT, NUT, SHADE, AND FOREST TREES. Owing to the subterranean habits of termites it is extremely difficult to prevent or remedy injury to individual living forest, fruit, or shade trees. In the case of shade trees the infestation may start as local at the base and extend more generally through the heartwood and sometimes to the top of the tree and through branches. A wise preventive measure is the removal and prompt burning of all loose wood which may afford shelter to termites, such as prunings, dead and dying trees and the like, and untreated fence posts and similar material. Care should be taken that trees do not become scarred near the base, in order to prevent heartrot and subsequent termite infestation. Clean forest, orchard, and horticultural management is to be recommended.

Properly executed tree surgery may sometimes be effective in repairing damage to valuable old trees. The infested dead heartwood should be cut out and the remaining heartwood brushed with coal tar creosote, taking care that no area nearer than one inch to the living sapwood is treated; then the cavity should be filled with suitable material.

Since termites in the southern states render unmerchantable the forest trees which have been killed by insects, fire, or disease, all timber from such trees should be utilized or removed as promptly as possible in areas where termites are common.

COVERING SCARS AND PRUNED AREAS. To prevent infestation, care should be taken that the trees do not become scarred, especially near the base. Scars and all pruned areas should be treated with a mixture of one-fourth creosote and three-fourths coal tar. This mixture should not be allowed to come in contact with the living tissues at the edges of the bark; to protect them a shellac should be applied.

COMMERCIAL FERTILIZERS. Soil heavily manured will attract subterranean termites, since they can obtain food from the animal manure; commercial fertilizers should be used in preference in regions where termites are common in the soil. The stimulation of plant growth after injury, especially callus about scars, by any means such as soil fertilization will prove helpful in protection from further injury.

POISON DUSTS. Often great damage is caused by dry-wood termites to the trunks and branches of living trees before the injury becomes apparent on the exterior of the trees. For several years attempts have been made to develop a suitable field microphone with which to detect the working of dry-wood termites in living trees before great damage has been caused. Damage to the trunks of tea bushes in Ceylon is usually great before the presence of the termites is discovered. If the termites could be detected working in trees, poison dust could be blown into their galleries through holes bored in the trunks and much injury prevented. So far no suitable field apparatus has been developed by the various agencies to which the problem was presented. A cheap, effective " fool-proof " apparatus that could be used by unskilled labor would save much money to tea planters in the Orient.

It has been proven in the tropics — in the case of tea bushes in Ceylon and citrus fruit trees in southern Florida and California — that dry-wood termites can be killed in infested trees by the use of poison dusts, such as Paris green at the rate of only one half an ounce per individual tree. Such injury to living trees has been remedied by boring holes in the trunks of the infested trees and blowing dry Paris green into the galleries of the termites by means of a bellows. If, because of moisture, the Paris green becomes caked, the treatment must be repeated, since for obvious reasons only the dry dust is effective.

YOUNG PLANTATION, ORCHARD, OR NURSERY STOCK. Termites are occasionally injurious in plantations, orchards, and nurseries. Injury to nursery stock will be more serious on recently cleared land, to stock from one to three years old, and where decaying wood is abundant. Any débris in which the insects breed should be removed. In general the use of recently cleared land should be avoided in planting stock. Earth used in banking should be free from rotten wood. Care should be taken not to allow the roots to dry out before planting, as weakened stock is especially susceptible to attack; particular care should be given grafted stock. In the case of the pecan it is recommended that two or three cereal crops be grown on newly cleared land before the young trees are set out.

Termites have also become pests in old orchards in both Florida and California, due to neglect. Vigilance and clean culture are preventive measures.

TREE SURGERY. As previously recommended, properly executed tree surgery sometimes is effective in repairing injury to valuable old fruit and shade trees.

INSECTICIDES. When valuable trees are infested but not yet dying, subterranean termites can be killed in the soil, if it is moist and not too compact, by breaking it up near the tree and pouring carbon disulphide on the earth at a distance of about a foot from the trunk, then covering the liquid over with earth. The gas from this liquid will penetrate the subterranean galleries of the termites. It is somewhat dangerous to plant life and very large doses should not be used. *Care should be taken*

*in handling this volatile fluid, as the gas or vapor from it is
highly inflammable and explosive when mixed with air in certain proportions; no flame should be brought near it, and the
fumes should not be inhaled, as they are poisonous.* There are
indications that an emulsion of carbon disulphide, which is on
the market ready for use, may prove more effective than carbon
disulphide alone; as in the case of the disulphide itself, the
earth is loosened up and the emulsion poured on, at least a foot
from the tree. Carbon tetrachloride can be similarly used but
is apparently not so effective as carbon disulphide. It is a thin,
transparent, colorless, volatile liquid, which forms a gas with a
pungent, aromatic odor. Like carbon disulphide it is heavier
than air. Although it is only about one-half or one-third as
effective as carbon disulphide when used at the same dosage
rate, it has the great advantage that its gas is neither explosive
nor inflammable; there will be no fire risk attending its use.
The gases from carbon disulphide and carbon tetrachloride,
being heavier than air, will not readily rise.

VINEYARDS. In vineyards all dead or diseased vines should be
removed as a part of clean management. All exposed areas left
by pruning should be painted with preservative coatings and
the prunings should be burned promptly. Near-by stands of
tree windbreaks should be carefully cared for and kept free from
infestation by termites. Trellis posts should be impregnated
with coal tar creosote before being placed in the ground.

FIELD AND TRUCK CROPS. Deep, late fall plowing will be of
value in breaking up the galleries and nests of subterranean
termites on ground planted to field or truck crops. Irrigation
of the land, where practicable, will be effective; this can be done
before planting the crop.

BURNING STUBBLE. Care should be taken not to plow under
stubble which will serve as food for termites; it should be
burned. The use of commercial fertilizers instead of animal
manure is also recommended where subterranean termites are
common in the soil.

ROTATION OF CROPS. As a result of the frequent stirring of
the soil, rotation of crops will aid in preventing termites from
injuring them. Plowing and fallowing are more practical than
the use of insecticides in preparing the soil to prevent termite
injury.

FLOWERS AND GREENHOUSE STOCK. Proper construction of greenhouses will practically safeguard plants growing in them from all injury by termites. Iron frames and concrete work should, wherever possible, replace bricks or woodwork. In cases of infestation of old greenhouses already built all wooden uprights supporting wooden plant benches should be sawed off, if set on or in the ground, and rested on stone, bricks, or concrete, above the surface of the ground. Proper repairing, including the removal of all infested wood, will prevent the plants from becoming infested in turn. Where woodwork is necessary the wood should be impregnated with zinc chloride or other toxic salt; it can be painted after treatment. Wood impregnated with coal tar creosote cannot be used with safety in greenhouses.

AVOIDING STABLE MANURE. In flower gardens, especially those located near the woodwork of buildings, commercial fertilizers should be substituted for stable manure in order to protect not only the buildings but also the growing plants.

INSECTICIDES. Either carbon disulphide or carbon tetrachloride can be used to kill termites in the soil if it is moist and not compact. Small holes should be made near the infested plants (not closer than 6 inches) and a small quantity of the liquid chosen poured in and the holes immediately closed tightly with earth. Calcium cyanide (two ounces to one square yard of ground is recommended) has also been found effective, but it should not be placed near living plants. It mixes readily with and enriches the soil and gives off an insecticidal gas which *should not be inhaled, as it is poisonous to human beings.* If it is desired, the plants can be temporarily removed while the soil is being treated with these gases.

An effective control may be found in the use of kerosene nicotine oleate or a 5 per cent kerosene emulsion. Kerosene emulsion is made as follows: kerosene, two gallons; fish-oil soap, one-half pound; water, one gallon. Dissolve the soap in hot water and pour in the oil slowly, with constant stirring to emulsify. Dilution: if 37 gallons of water be added to the above stock emulsion it will give 40 gallons of 5 per cent kerosene emulsion.

If the greenhouse benches are infested, but for any reason cannot be replaced, they should be soaked thoroughly with this emulsion, as should also the ashes and sand under the pots on the benches. This may be done by removing the potted plants from a section of the bench, spraying that section, and moving the pots on the bench to cover the treated area, thus giving access to another section. Potted heliotropes and geraniums have been treated directly with the 5 per cent kerosene emulsion without injury to the plants, and the termites in the soil of the pots were all killed. The soil should be wet down before this spray is used. This treatment should be given late in the afternoon and be followed early the next morning with a thorough syringing of the soil with water to wash out the surplus oil. It is important to remove all infested pots from the bench as soon as the infestation is noticed and to destroy the termites with kerosene emulsion.

APPENDIX

SPECIFICATIONS FOR REMEDYING TERMITE DAMAGE TO VARIOUS TYPES OF BUILDINGS

TERMITE damage to the woodwork of buildings can be remedied by the householder himself or by the employment of an intelligent contractor. Common sense and not the services of an expert are needed to put into effect the following recommendations. However, it is always advisable to outline the scope of the work necessary in repairing the various types of buildings damaged by termites. Indeed, often it is well to have a contract drawn up. The following suggestions are suitable for remedying the normal termite damage in buildings of the average types, and afford the basis for such contracts. Sometimes, it is necessary to call for expert advice on reconstruction based on a knowledge of termites.

TYPE OF CONSTRUCTION

I. Where wooden floors, foundation timbers, architraves (uprights or joists), sills, porches, steps, sleepers laid in concrete, etc., are in contact with the earth.

SCOPE OF WORK. Remove from basement or cellar the present wood floors, sleepers, filling between sleepers, wood wainscot, wooden thresholds, wooden subsills, window stools, partitions, baseboards, stairs, and the coal bin.

Excavate or fill in basement, or cellar, where wood floors are removed, as may be necessary to bring sub-grade to depth of four inches below level of present floors.

Form cement coves, thresholds and bases where cement paving is to be done and in other locations when hereinafter specified.

Remove all old wood forms where same are found still remaining in place. All old boards, wood scraps, débris, and any other materials that will attract termites, now located throughout the basement and unexcavated areas under the building, shall be entirely removed from the premises by the contractor. Débris, etc., specified to be removed from the premises shall be carried to a dump and burned.

In basement, or cellar, shore up, if necessary for removal of uprights, cut-off bottom ends and replace on cast iron bases. Cut off bottom of door jambs and architraves in basement.

All new wood studs, furring strips, wood lath and other similar new woodwork unexposed after installation and all new structural timbers shall be treated in an approved manner with standard (Federal specifications) chemical preservatives to render the wood more resistant to attack by termites. Preservatives used shall not injure or affect wood, plaster and marble or the finish on wood and plaster which is directly or indirectly in contact with the wood so treated.

PAVING, ETC. Cement shall be of an approved brand or a mortar composed of 1 part Portland cement to 3 parts of sand graded from fine to coarse, with no grains larger than will pass through the No. 10 sieve, to which may be added 10 per cent by weight of the cement or some workability agent, such as hydrated lime.

Sand shall be clean and sharp, free from loam or vegetable matter and preferably with grains varying in size.

Stone shall be hard and durable and broken so as not to exceed two inches in any direction. Clean, washed gravel of the same size may be used instead of stone.

Remove partitions, stairs, floors and sleepers in basement or cellar; excavate or fill, as may be necessary, to bring earth to even surface of four inches below top of present floor. Lay a paving base three and one quarter inches thick, composed of one part cement, three parts sand and six parts broken stone or gravel. Before concrete base has set, apply a smooth top dressing three quarters of an inch thick, composed of two parts of cement and three parts sand or fine granite screenings (not dust). All expansion joints shall be filled with coal tar pitch. All thresholds shall be formed of top dressing mixture and troweled to a smooth surface.

Where plastered walls are furred or stripped, cut away plaster, studs or stripping to a height of six inches above floor and build a cement base tight against brick wall and flush with face of plastering.

Cut off lower part of door jambs and casing six inches above floor and replace with cement plinths. These plinths shall project one quarter inch beyond jambs and casing and shall be offset so as to properly receive the architraves. Sink down strips of metal from woodwork into concrete.

All cement plinths, bases, etc., shall be reinforced with heavy wire lath well anchored to walls.

Between cement plastered walls and cement bases and paving form a cement cove or sanitary finish with radius of one inch.

In basement or cellar, where necessary move steam pipe on floor along wall and form cement cove, with radius of one inch, between plastered wall and paving. Replace pipe, using offset connections if necessary.

PLASTERING. Where wood wainscot and wood base are removed in basement or cellar, patch, if necessary, and white-coat and make a neat job where plastering joins new cement base; patch with gypsum two-coat work, to finish even with surface of present work.

PAINTING. Baseboards, plinths or other concrete work shall be suitably painted to match plaster or woodwork.

TYPE OF CONSTRUCTION

II. Where filled-in porches, steps, etc., are in contact with the main building and joists from the main building project into such earth-filled areas; or where there are unexcavated areas under floors.

SCOPE OF WORK. Remove the earth and wood débris from the filled-in areas, cutting through foundations if necessary. Separate the main building from the filled-in porch, etc., by means of a concrete wall or barrier.

Space under floors near the earth shall be excavated so that there will be no earth within 18 inches of the wood. They shall be provided with cross-ventilation openings proportioned on the basis of 2 square feet for each 25 linear feet of exterior wall, except that such openings need not be placed in the front of such building. Each opening shall be provided with 20-mesh noncorroding screening.

Or poison the soil under the building after digging a trench 30 inches deep (in no case lower than the top of footing), and at least 12 inches wide at the top, around the foundation walls and piers, in all unexcavated areas, removing all wood débris and breaking off all earth-like shelter tubes over foundations. Saturate the soil at the bottom of the trench with full strength orthodichlorobenzene at the rate of one gallon per ten linear feet, replace the soil and repeat the treatment within 3 inches of the surface.

If this chemical is used in a closed area, the operator should not remain for too long a time subject to the fumes. If possible, secure good ventilation while this chemical is being used. Care should be taken not to let the liquid come in contact with the face and hands since it might slightly burn and would be especially painful if it got into the eyes.

In cases where there is danger of orthodichlorobenzene reaching the spreading roots of living vegetation, use paradichlorobenzene in the crystalline form in the same manner as specified above.

Crystals shall be used at the rate of approximately 5 pounds per 10 linear feet. Or use a mixture of one part coal tar creosote and three parts kerosene oil at the rate of one gallon of this mixture per ten linear feet.

TYPE OF CONSTRUCTION

III. Where buildings are on masonry foundations in the form of walls or piers, and earth-like shelter tubes of termites are extended over these foundations to reach untreated wood above.

SCOPE OF WORK. Break off the shelter tubes and insert metal termite shields or barriers on the foundations. Such shields shall continue completely around the top of the masonry foundation, including all pillars, inside and outside surfaces. A shield may be formed of a strip of noncorroding metal (such as copper, or zinc, or an alloy composed of 28 per cent of copper, 67 per cent of nickel, and 5 per cent of iron, manganese, and silicon) firmly inserted in the surface of the masonry, or between the foundations and the wood; the upper tier of bricks or other unit shall be removed if necessary. The projecting edge shall be bent downward at an angle of 45 degrees and shall extend horizontally at least 2 inches from the face of the foundation. In masonry buildings this shield can be inset in the masonry at a height at least 18 inches above the ground.

Or poison the earth about the walls and piers as directed on page 166.

TYPE OF CONSTRUCTION

IV. Where poor grades of mortar are being penetrated by termites either boring horizontally between masonry units in walls or piers or coming up longitudinally through hollow units.

SCOPE OF WORK. Wall in basement, cellar or foundations shall be plastered from concrete cove at floor to ceiling with two coats of Portland cement plaster, one inch thick, as follows:

Rake out mortar joints to a depth of at least one-half inch. When plaster is applied the surface of wall must be clean, free from dust, dirt and other loose particles and thoroughly wetted. The plaster shall be mixed in the proportions of one sack of Portland cement to three cubic feet of clean sharp sand, and shall contain hydrated lime in an amount not to exceed 10% by volume of the cement in the mixture (1 to 3 to 10% lime). Outside walls shall be treated in same manner.

In basement, top off walls where present wood sills and stools are to be removed with a coat of cement plaster one inch thick.

Inspector———— RECORD OF TERMITE DAMAGE Date————

BUILDING

Town———— Street———— Class of building————

Age of building———— Type of construction————

Height of foundation above grade———— Foundation material————

Ventilation area———— Height of sub-floor space————
(Open or closed)

Wooden porch———— Wooden steps————

DAMAGE

(A) BY TERMITES:

Timbers on foundations———— In mud sills————

In under-pinning in sub-floor or floor———— In studs————

Plates———— Beams———— Sleepers———— Base-boards————

In wooden porches———— In wooden steps————

Damage superficial———— Structural weakening————

(B) BY POWDER-POST BEETLES:————

(C) BY DECAY: Alone————; decay associated with termites————

REPAIRS

CONTROL BY:
1. Inspection and breaking off shelter tubes and removal of wood débris————
2. By soil poisoning: Liquid———— Crystals————
3. Quantity per linear foot————
4. Structural repairs: (Give details on back of sheet with diagram)————
5. Replaced wood should be chemically impregnated———— or not————

REMARKS:

Where hollow masonry units have been used in foundations, cap the top of the walls or piers below the wooden sill with Portland cement, plaster or mortar one inch thick. Where mortar has disintegrated in brick walls or piers cap them similarly.

A frame building need not be raised or jacked up to cap the wall, but the upper tier of bricks or other unit can be removed, a few at a time, and the wall capped.

Where it is impractical to cap hollow masonry units, such as tile or concrete blocks, bore holes in these units and pour in liquid orthodichlorobenzene at the rate of one gallon per 10 linear feet.

Any cracks, crevices, or voids in concrete floors or walls shall be repaired; special attention shall be given where wood rests on flooring or wall and any cracks repaired.

PROVISIONS FOR CITY BUILDING CODES FOR INSURING PROTECTION AGAINST TERMITES AND DECAY

1. Wood or fiber products, when not impregnated with an approved preservative, shall not be placed in contact with the earth or within 18 inches thereof, excepting wood columns or posts over a concrete floor, which columns shall be provided with noncorroding metal or concrete base plates or footings 6 inches above the floor. This applies to steps, which shall be laid over a concrete base, projecting at least 6 inches beyond the supports of the steps.

2. Timber to be used in contact with the earth shall be thoroughly impregnated by a standard pressure process with coal tar creosote or other equivalent preservative. Timber should be completely framed before treatment, whenever possible, but when cutting after treatment is unavoidable, the cut surfaces shall be thoroughly coated with coal tar creosote or other equivalent preservative.

3. Masonry foundations and footings shall be laid in Portland cement mortar. Foundations built up of masonry units, whether hollow or solid, shall be *capped below woodwork* with at least 1 inch of Portland cement mortar, or the mortar and slate, or solid or joined noncorroding metal, or other equally efficient seal.

4. In the case of frame buildings, a metal termite shield or mechanical barrier shall be provided, continuing completely around the top of the masonry foundation, including all pillars, supports, and piping, below the woodwork of the building, on both the inside and outside surfaces. Such a shield may be formed of a strip of noncorroding metal (such as copper, zinc, or an alloy of copper 28%, nickel 67%, iron, manganese, and silicon 5%), firmly

inserted in the surface of the masonry, or between the foundation and the wood, with the projecting edge bent downward at an angle of 45 degrees and extending horizontally at least 2 inches from the face of the foundation. In masonry buildings this shield can be inset in the masonry at a height at least 18 inches above the ground.

5. Floor sleepers or joists imbedded in masonry or concrete, or laid on concrete which is in contact with the earth, shall be impregnated with an approved preservative.

6. Expansion joints between concrete floor and wall shall be filled with coal tar pitch and the right angle joint covered with a sanitary cement mortar or Portland cement concrete finish of an arc of at least 2 inches in length.

7. The ends of wood beams or girders entering masonry or concrete shall not be sealed in but shall be provided with boxes affording an air space at the end of the piece of not less than 1 inch at side of member, unless the ends of such timbers are impregnated with coal tar creosote or other approved preservative.

8. Where only a portion of the space under the house is to be excavated for cellar or basement rooms, the balance, including sun parlors, porches, etc., should be excavated so that there will be no earth within 18 inches of the wood, and this area should also be provided with cross-ventilation. Such ventilating openings shall be proportioned on the basis of 2 square feet for each 25 linear feet of exterior wall, except that such opening need not be placed in front of such building. Each opening shall be provided with 20-mesh noncorroding metal screening, including windows in attics.

9. Where timber is used in roofs of the flat type, the roof shall, unless protected on the weather side with a covering impervious to water, have a slope and runoff sufficient to provide proper drainage.

10. All wooden forms on foundations shall be removed from masonry work within 15 days: grading stakes should be removed before laying concrete floors.

NOTE: Paragraphs 1, 2, 3, 4, and 8 are essential.

ADDENDA

ADDENDA

IN Table I will be found a list of the living and fossil termites of the world, classified by families. This shows the relatively larger number of primitive fossil termites than the more specialized forms and in contrast the comparatively larger number of living specialized forms than the living primitive or generalized forms.

Table II lists the termites of the United States by families, genera, and species. It also shows the groups or types into which they fall, based on their habits; this classification is necessary before control measures can be recommended or instituted. Both tables are dated, since new species are constantly being discovered and described. The tables are up to date as of June, 1935.

TABLE I

ISOPTERA OF THE WORLD

FAMILY	LIVING	FOSSIL [1]
Mastotermitidae	1	10
Hodotermitidae	29	8
Kalotermitidae	319	22
Rhinotermitidae	174	9
Termitidae	1392	14
	1915	63
	Grand Total	1978

[1] Including termites found in stone, Baltic and Burmese amber and gum copal.

TABLE II

ISOPTERA OF THE UNITED STATES

(Total Number of Species 56)

This list groups our native termites not only by their scientific classification ranging from the primitive to the specialized forms, but also by their habits or structure. However, it must be remembered that the damp-wood termites are occasionally subterranean and burrow in the earth near tree roots. The Florida *Prorhinotermes* is in reality a damp-wood termite, only occasionally burrowing into the soil. The nasutiform, desert, and soldierless termites are subterranean in habit.

FAMILY KALOTERMITIDAE (total number of species 22):

Rotten-wood termites

- Zoötermopsis angusticollis Hag. — light, Pacific Coast rotten-wood termite
- " laticeps Bks. — southwestern rotten-wood termite
- " nevadensis Hag. — dark, Pacific Coast rotten-wood termite

Dry-wood termites

- Kalotermes (Kalotermes) approximatus Sny. — dark, eastern dry-wood termite
- " " arizonensis Sny.
- " " banski Sny.
- " " hubbardi Bks. — light, Pacific Coast dry-wood termite
- " " jouteli Bks.
- " " lighti Sny.
- " " minor Hag. — dark, Pacific Coast dry-wood termite
- " " minor Hag. form varius Sny.
- " " occidentis Walk. — large, primitive dry-wood termite
- " " schwarzi Bks. — southern dry-wood termite
- " " snyderi Light — light, eastern dry-wood termite
- " " texanus Bks.
- " " new species

Damp-wood termites

- " (Neotermes) angustoculus Sny. — southern damp-wood termite
- " " castaneus Burm. — southern damp-wood termite
- " (Paraneotermes) simplicicornis Bks. — arid land dry-wood termite

Powder-post termites

- " (Cryptotermes) brevis Walk. — tropical rough-headed powder-post termite
- " " cavifrons Bks.
- " (Calcaritermes) nearcticus Sny.

FAMILY RHINOTERMITIDAE (total number of species 13):

Subterranean termites

- Prorhinotermes simplex Hag. — Florida Prorhinotermes
- Heterotermes aureus Sny. — desert subterranean termite
- Reticulitermes arenicola Goellner — sand-dwelling subterranean termite
- " claripennis Bks. — clear-winged subterranean termite
- " flavipes Kol. — eastern subterranean termite
- " hageni Bks. — light, southern subterranean termite
- " hesperus Bks. — Pacific Coast subterranean termite
- " humilis Bks. — southwestern subterranean termite
- " lucifugus Rossi — European subterranean termite
- " tibialis Bks. — arid land subterranean termite
- " tumiceps Bks. — swollen-headed subterranean termite
- " virginicus Bks. — southern subterranean termite
- " new species

FAMILY TERMITIDAE (total number of species 22):

Nasutiform termites

- Nasutitermes (Nasutitermes) costaricensis Holmg.
- " (Tenuirostritermes) cinereus Buckley
- " " tenuirostris Desn.

Desert termites

- Amitermes (Amitermes) coachellae Light — Coachella desert termite
- " " emersoni Light — Emerson desert termite
- " " minimus Light
- " " pallidus Light
- " " parvipunctus Light
- " " parvulus Light
- " " silvestrianus Light — Silvestri desert termite
- " " snyderi Light — Snyder desert termite
- " " spadix Light
- " " wheeleri Dean. — Wheeler desert termite
- " (Gnathamitermes) acrognathus Light
- " " acutus Light
- " " confusus Bks.
- " " fuscus Light
- " " infumatus Light
- " " magnoculus Light
- " " perplexus Bks.
- " " tubiformans Buckley — tube-building desert termite

Soldierless termites

} Anoplotermes (Anoplotermes) fumosus Hagen.

TABLE III

CLASSIFICATION OF TERMITE GUESTS OR INQUILINES

Groups	Treatment
Parasites, internal or external.	Apparently unobserved by termites.
Predators, which feed on eggs, young or adult termites.	Persecuted by the termites.
Scavengers, which feed on refuse or nest material.	Tolerated by termites.
Guests with no special adaptation for colony life, but which give exudate.	Attended by termites.
True guests with structural adaptation for giving exudate: physogastric forms.	Specially cared for by termites.

GLOSSARY

GLOSSARY

Herewith is appended a glossary of technical terms. Where possible the definitions have been made to apply to termites or associated forms of life. Some terms have been modified for this special use from the *Explanation of Terms Used in Entomology* by H. B. Smith, 1906; others have been taken directly from this useful book.

ABDOMEN: the third or posterior portion of the insect body, usually consisting of nine or ten apparent segments; the abdomen is connected to the head by the thorax or that portion bearing the wings and legs.

ADULT: a mature individual of any caste or form of termite, either fertile or sterile.

AGGREGATION: close association of the same form of life in one place.

AMBER: a transparent, clear, pale yellowish-brown, fossilized vegetable resin.

ANTENNAE: two joined, articulate, sensory organs borne one on each side of the head, commonly called " feelers ".

ANTHROPOCENTRIC: a term applied to attempts to correlate insect behavior with man's actions or reactions, or the endowing of insects with man-like faculties.

ANUS: the end of the digestive tract through which the excreta are passed, opening at the posterior of the abdomen.

APTEROUS: adjective characterizing a termite nymph (third form) or the reproductive form which develops from such a nymph, which is wingless and never possesses either wings or wing pads.

ARBOREAL: living in, on, or among trees.

ARCHAIC: ancient, no longer dominant.

ARTICULATE: divided into joints or segments.

ASYMMETRICAL: not alike on the two sides; not symmetrical.

BACTERIA: low forms of plant life, microscopic organisms, some of which are found in the intestines of termites.

BALANCE OF NATURE: a state of equilibrium where all factors, plant, animal, etc., in the environment serve to counterbalance or offset each other and are in a perfect interrelationship, or life under control.

BRACHYPTEROUS: adjective characterizing a termite nymph (second form) and the reproductive form which develops from such a nymph, which never possesses wings but has short or abbreviated wing pads.

BREEDING: sexually uniting male and female termites to obtain young.

CARTON NEST: an ovoid or semi-spherical termite nest hard or soft in texture, constructed of digested, excreted cellulose and earth or mostly of earth.

CASTE: a form or kind of mature termite adapted for special duties, as workers, soldiers, reproductive forms; a single species may have several different types of the same caste, as major, intermediate, and minor soldiers, major and minor workers, etc.

CAUDAL: pertaining to the posterior or anal extremity.

CELLULOSE: the chief constituent of wood and the principal food of termites.

CHORDOTONAL ORGANS: organs of special sense responsive to vibrations.

CHROMOSOMES: microscopic color bodies, part of the cell nucleus, which bear the inheritable characters.

CLASSIFICATION: the systematic arrangement of insects (or other animals or plants) in series showing their relation or agreement in structure, life habits or other characters forming the basis of the " classification ".

COLONY: a group of termites of various castes living permanently together in the same nest or community, all forms working for the welfare of the whole group rather than the individual.

CONIDIA: small, globular spores or fruiting bodies of fungi (low forms of plant life) cultivated for food by termites.

COPULATION: the sexual union of a male and female and the merging of the male and female elements leading to the fertilization of the female.

CORRELATE: to bring together into relation.

COSMOPOLITAN: occurring throughout most of the world.

CRYPTOBIOTIC: " hidden life ", a term applied to insects, such as termites, living a life where they are concealed in wood, underground, etc.

DEÄLATED: the male or female reproductive adult after the wings have been shed.

DEFAUNATED: the loss of the intestinal fauna of termites (such as bacteria or pro-tozoa) , induced either naturally or by artificial means.

DIFFUSED: spread out over a wide area, in contrast to *concentrated.*

DORSAL: belonging to the upper surface, in contrast to *ventral,* the lower surface.

" DRY ROT ": a disintegration of wood to a dry, crumbly condition caused by low forms of plant life or wood-destroying fungi.

ECOLOGY: the science of the relation of organisms to each other or to their en-vironment (surroundings) .

ENTOMOLOGY: that branch of Zoölogy (study of animal life) that deals with insects.

ENVIRONMENT: the sum of the influences surrounding or acting upon an organism.

EXCREMENT: waste products discharged from the anus.

EXCRETION: the act of getting rid of waste products; also any material or substance produced by secretory glands or structures and voided or otherwise sent out from them.

EXOTIC: not a native of the place where found.

EXUDATE: secretion or gland excretion from the bodies of termites or guests of termites eagerly solicited as food by one termite from another or interchanged between termites and guests in the nest.

FAMILY: a division of classification of life including a number of genera (major groups) agreeing in one or a set of characteristics and so closely related that they are apparently descended from one stem.

FAUNA: the assemblage of animals inhabiting a region or country.

FERTILIZATION: the merging of the male element with the female element within the egg cell.

FLAGELLATE: applied to protozoa with whip-like appendages.

FLORA: the assemblage of plant life inhabiting a region or country.

FOSSIL: a form of life preserved in stone, amber, etc., usually not also to be found living but preserved as a relic of a former age.

FRONTAL GLAND: a gland located on the front of the head of termites opening as a small pore or extended as a beak-like process; a sticky secretion exudes from this gland which is useful as a " chemical warfare " defense against ants; this gland probably evolved from the ancestral median simple eye.

FUNGI: low forms of plant life; wood-destroying fungi produce thread-like elements (mycelia) and toadstool-like fruiting bodies.

FUNGUS GARDENS: ovoid chambers in the nests of certain African and Oriental termites in which fungi or mushrooms are raised as food.

GENERALIZED: primitive, simple, containing in combination characters that are separated and specialized in other forms.

GENUS: a major group of kinds, or an assemblage of species agreeing in some one character or series of characters; usually considered as arbitrary and opinionative, though some consider it a natural assemblage.

GREGARIOUS: living in societies or communities, but not social.

GROOMING: the licking of the body of one termite by another to obtain exudate or secretions.

GUEST: " inquiline ", a term applied to those insects that live in nests or dwelling places of other species, not necessarily at the expense of the host (see Table III) .

GYNANDROMORPHIC: a term used when an individual of one sex exhibits on one lateral half the organic characters of the other sex, more or less completely.

HABITAT: the region or place which an insect inhabits or where it was taken.

HEAD: the first or anterior region or division of the insect body, attached to the thorax, bearing the mouth parts (structures) and antennae.

HERMAPHRODITE: an individual in which the characters of both sexes are combined.

HUMERAL SUTURE: the line of weakness at the base of the wing where the wing breaks off after the flight.

HYBRID: the progeny from the mating of two species.

IMAGO: the adult or sexually developed insect.

INCUBATION: hatching or developing of an egg, or period of hatching.

INQUILINE: a form of life living in the nests of termites, a guest (see Table III).

INTERCASTE: an individual of a species having body characters of two forms or castes; an intermediate.

INSTINCT: in insects, a collection of tropisms (reactions) or behavior resulting from the effects of stimuli.

INTERMEDIATE: lying between others in position, or possessing characters between two other forms.

ISOPTERA: equal-winged — an ordinal term for insects with four similar net-veined wings; mouth mandibulate; thoracic rings similar, loosely jointed; metamorphosis incomplete. Termites.

KING: the deälated male termite or male winged termite after the loss of the wings, or the mature brachypterous or apterous male termite.

LABIUM: the lower lip which forms the floor of the mouth, in contrast to the labrum or upper lip.

LABRUM: the upper lip; covers the base of the mandible and forms the roof of the mouth.

LARVA: the young of an insect having a complete " metamorphosis ", or one that passes through a pupal period (long resting stage) to the adult form.

LATERAL: relating, pertaining, or attached to the side.

LIGNIN: a constituent of wood which passes through the intestines of termites without being digested.

MACROPTEROUS: winged termites, the reproductive first form adults with long wings, in contrast to the brachypterous or short winged second forms with short wing pads or the apterous wingless third form reproductive adults; the latter two forms are termed " complementary " reproductive forms.

MANDIBLES: the lateral upper jaws of a biting insect.

MANDIBULATE: with jaws or mandibles.

MATING: see PAIRING.

MENDELISM: a law or rule governing the inheritance of characters in plants and animals, discovered by Gregor Mendel. This principle deals with inheritance of "unit characters", presence or absence of one or other of a pair of contrasting characters, dominant and recessive. It also shows that the offspring of organisms with a pair of contrasting characters will exhibit these in a definite ratio, and it is extended to deal with groups of characters.

MESONOTUM: the middle division of the thorax.

METABOLISM: transformation, the whole process or series of changes of food into tissue and cell-substance and of these latter into waste products.

METAMORPHOSIS: the series of changes through which an insect passes in the growth from egg to adult.

METANOTUM: the posterior divisions of the thorax.

MOLT: a period in the transformation from one stage to another; usually the skin is shed.

MONOGAMY: a union in which one male fertilizes only one female.

MUTATION: gradual variation toward a definite change of structure; discontinuous variation; the theory of DeVries that new forms, differing sufficiently to constitute a new variety, arise spontaneously and remain true.

MYIASIS: disease or injury caused by the attack of dipterous (fly) larvae.

MYRMECOPHILOUS: ant-loving, a term applied to insects that live in ant nests.

NANISM: a dwarfed condition of body due to lack of food in sufficient quantity, particularly noticeable in the soldier caste in young colonies of termites, before enough workers are reared to provide the colony with an abundance of food.

NASUS: a beak or nose-like process on the front of the head of certain termites, at the apex of which is the opening of the frontal gland.

NASUTI: that type of termite soldiers that have the head prolonged into a point.

NASUTIFORM: termites with soldiers having a nose-like process or nasus on the front of the head at the apex of which opens the frontal gland from which exudes a secretion used in defense; mandibles may also be present or absent.

NEARCTIC: temperate and arctic North America, including Greenland.

NEMATODES: round worms often found as internal parasites of termites.

NEOTEINIC: applied to complemental females among termites because, though reproductive, they retain some juvenile characters.

NEPHROCYTES: cells which secrete waste and then migrate to the surface of the body to discharge.

NEUTER: a sterile worker or soldier termite.

NODULE: a little knot, lump or node.

NYMPH: the young or immature termite.

OCELLUS: a simple eye, consisting of a single convex or bead-like lens, which conveys an image to a retina. Ocelli occur in termites in pairs, one near each compound eye; the compound eyes are made up of numerous ocelli.

OLFACTORY: pertaining to the sense of smell.

ONTOGENY: the development of the individual as distinguished from that of the species; see PHYLOGENY.

ORDER: one of the primary divisions of the Class *Insecta,* based largely on wing structure and usually ending in *-ptera.*

PAEDOGENESIS: reproduction in the sexually immature or larval stage.

PAIRING: mating, the association of male and female termites, often " in tandem ", after the flight and the loss of the wings, for the purpose of founding new colonies, but prior to copulation.

PARASITIC: living on or in some other animal or insect in such a way as to derive all nourishment from the tissues of the host.

PARTHENOGENESIS: reproduction by direct growth of germs from egg-cells without fertilization by the male element; as in plant lice, gall wasps, etc.

PEDICLE: see PETIOLE.

PELLETS: small rod-like lumps of excrement of dry-wood termites, impressed or sculptured, which become hardened after leaving the anus.

PETIOLE: a stem or stalk; specifically, the slender segment between the thorax and abdomen in many ants and bees and some *Diptera,* or flies; also termed pedicle.

PHYLOGENY: the development of a group of species, in contrast to ontogeny or the development of an individual; the history of the physical evolution, or the tracing back of the origin of a group.

PHYSOGASTRIC: that post-adult stage in insects in which the abdomen is greatly enlarged; sometimes the swollen abdomen is inverted over the thorax (the portion of the body bearing legs and wings) ; old termite queens and certain insect guests in the nests of termites often become markedly physogastric.

POLYGAMY: the mating of a male with more than one female.

POLYMORPHISM OR POLYMORPHIC: the presence of different forms or castes of termites of the same species; i.e., workers, soldiers, and reproductive forms.

POST-ADULT GROWTH: a unique growth of the body of termites and certain insect guests undergone after the adult winged stage has been reached and leading to physogastric shape.

PREDACEOUS: a term applied to insects that live by preying upon other organisms.

PROGENY: the young resulting from copulation and fertilization.

PROCTODEAL FOOD: food in semi-liquid form received from the anus.

PRONOTUM: the anterior division of the thorax.

PROTOTYPE: a primitive form to which later forms can be traced.

PROTOZOA: microscopic organisms or low forms of animal life; forms occurring in the intestines of termites are never " free living " or found elsewhere.

GLOSSARY

Pseudo-flight: attempts of the second form (brachypterous) reproductive adults, with short wing pads and without wings, to fly at the same time as the flight of the winged adults; possibly this is a reversion to the ancestral habit or instinct to fly, for the most primitive ancestral termites or their prototypes probably were all winged and there was no caste system.

Queen: the deälated female winged adult or mature brachypterous or apterous adult.

Quiescent stage: a short period of resting during which termites pass through a molt or shed the skin or external skeleton; the motionless insect in this stage is usually doubled up or in a position with the head appressed to the ventral surface of the body.

Rearing: the raising of the young termites through the nymphal stages to the adult stages.

Rectum: a chamber, variable in size and form, just within the anus, in which the excreta are formed or moulded for expulsion from the body; cloaca.

Reticulate: like network.

Reversion: a return in a greater or less degree to some ancestral type; atavism.

Royal cell: usually a centrally located, domed cell in which the king and queen termites are tended by workers or young; in certain tropical termites the royal pair are immobile and are actually imprisoned.

Royal pair: Royalties — the sexually active males and females of social insects.

Saliva: the secretion of the salivary glands that moistens and begins the digestion of food.

Sculptured: a term describing a surface marked with elevations or depressions, or both, arranged in some definite manner.

Segregants; segregation: in the Mendelian sense, dissociation of characters in the formation of germs.

Selective feeders: among wood-boring insects, those which have preferences for certain kinds of wood, in contrast to " general feeders ", which eat any kind of wood.

Sensory: relating to or having a sense function.

Serrate: saw-toothed; having the teeth set toward one end.

Shelter tubes: earth-like tubes constructed by termites from excreted wood and earth to serve as runways; such tubes conserve humidity, exclude light and many predaceous enemies.

Social insects: those living together permanently in more or less fixed organizations or large or small colonies, where there are several different forms or castes which all work for the welfare of the community. There is a more or less closely-adhered-to division of labor.

Soldiers: among termites these are sterile forms, or sexually undeveloped males and females, with the head variously modified for defense.

SPECIES: an aggregation of individuals alike in appearance and structure, mating freely and producing young that themselves mate freely and bear fertile offspring resembling each other and their parents: a species includes all its varieties and races.

SPECIALIZED: highly developed, complex types, especially adapted for definite purposes.

STAGE: refers to the period of development.

STERILE: not capable of reproducing its kind.

STOMODEAL FOOD: food regurgitated and fed from the mouth.

STYLI OR STYLETS: genital appendices on the ninth ventral segment of the abdomen of the young (and the male adult).

SUBSOCIAL: living a gregarious but not social life.

SUBTERRANEAN: underground or in the earth.

SWARMING: the seasonal flight of winged termites leading to dispersal and the formation of new colonies; it is essentially a colonizing flight and not a nuptial or marriage flight, as in ants and bees. After this flight and the loss of the wings, males and females associate to form new colonies; copulation takes place only after the nuptial cell is excavated.

SYMBIOSIS: a life relationship existing between different kinds of animals or plants, or between animals and plants; in true symbiosis both parties to the relationship benefit.

SYMBIOTIC: term describing species that live together in a state of symbiosis.

SYMMETRICAL: evenly developed on both sides.

SYSTEMATIST: one who classifies forms of life in definite order or arranges according to a system.

TERMITARIUM: a nest, natural or artificial, or a colony of termites.

TERRESTRIAL: living on or in the land; opposed to aquatic or arboreal.

THORAX: the second or intermediate division or region of the insect body, connecting the head and abdomen and bearing the wings and legs. The thorax is divided into the pronotum, the anterior portion; the mesonotum, or middle; and the metanotum, or posterior portion.

TROPHALLAXIS: an exchange of nourishment between individual termites or between termites and guests in the nest.

TROPISM: behavior of an animal in response to internal or external stimuli; i.e., phototropism, response to light; geotropism, response to earth; thigmotropism, response to contact. Tropisms may be either positive or negative reactions; grouped as a whole they constitute instinct.

VARIETY: any departure from the normal type of a species which, while retaining the specific characters, is yet recognizably different because of climatic, seasonal or other influences; a variety may occur with the type form or as a geographical race.

VENTRAL: pertaining to the under surface of the abdomen.

VESTIGIAL: small or degenerate; a trace or remnant of a previously functional organ.

WINGS OF THE HEART: the series of diagonal and other muscular fibers above the diaphragm in the pericardial cavity.

WING PADS: undeveloped, unfolded wings of varying length on the thorax of termite nymphs, brachypterous adults, and, rarely, on soldiers; rudimentary wings.

WING SCALE: the base of the wing where it is attached to the thorax, separated from the wing by a line of weakness (the humeral suture) where the wing breaks off, after the swarming flight.

ZOÖGRAPHICAL REGIONS: geographical regions or areas with the same general environment, including fauna and flora.

INDEX

Brachypterous adults, 23, 35 ff.
  See Reproductive adults
Breeding experiments, 59 ff.
British Columbia, 8, 9
Broods, termite, 54 ff.
Buckley, S. B., 77
Building Codes, municipal, 137–138, 169
Buildings,
  damage to, 107 ff.
  prevention of damage, 132 ff., 169–170
  remedies, 142 ff., 149 ff.
  specifications for remedying damage, 164 ff.
  types damaged, 132
Bureau of Entomology, vii–viii, 45, 87, 93, 104, 106, 110, 128, 137, 138, 147, 150
Bureau of Standards, 93

Calcium cyanide, 162
California, 9, 10, 13, 18, 69, 119
Camphor wood, 91
Canada, 8, 9
Canal Zone, 87 ff., 105, 135, 149–150
Cannibalism, 62, 84–85
Cape Henry, Va., 8, 9
Capping of walls, 134, 143–144, 169
Capritermes Wasmann, 30, 31, 32
Carbon disulphide, 132, 152, 160–161, 162
Carbon tetrachloride, 161, 162
Carboniferous measures, 15, 20
Carcoma, 7
Carpenter ants, 54, 80, 85, 98
Carton nests, 27, 64 ff.
Castes, termite, 2, 3, 6, 17, 18, 19, 22 ff.
Castle, G. B., 4
Cauliflower: *see* Conidia
Cellulose, 56, 80–83, 103
Cement, proper proportions to mix, 165
Cement mortar, use of, 92, 93, 167, 169
Centipeds, 96, 125
Central America, 9, 10, 86
Ceylon, 101, 159, 160
Chapman, F. M., 87
Charleston, S. C., 9
Chemical extractives in wood, 87 ff.
"Chemical warfare" by termites, 29–31
Chemicals: *see* Preservative treatments; Soil poisons; Fumigation; Spraying

"Chimneys", termite, 44, 49, 57
Chordotonal organs, 51
Chromosomes, 4
Citrus trees, injury to, 69, 100, 102, 117, 160
Classification,
  of termite guests, 95, 98, 176
  of termites, 6, 64
Cleveland, L. R., 16, 17, 40, 55, 60, 81, 103
Climate, effect of on termites, 10, 11, 105
Coal tar creosote, 134, 147, 148, 153–156, 159, 165
Coal tar pitch, 143, 165, 170
Coccinelid, 97
Cockroach, 12
Coffins, damage to, 115
Collapse of buildings, 129, 145, 146
Colonies, termite, 18, 48 ff., 64 ff.
Colonizing flight, 17, 39, 42 ff., 141
Colorado, 12, 13
Comejen, 7
Communication by termites, 28, 32, 51
Complementary reproductive forms, 23, 26, 39, 59, 61
Composition board, 89, 113, 148
Concrete, 93, 143, 165
Concrete floor, proper construction of, 143
Conidia, 54, 55
Conopid, 120
Construction,
  improper, 106, 109, 110, 131
  proper, 129, 139, 169, 170
  remedies, 142 ff., 164 ff.
  types of, 108, 132, 133
Control of termites: *see* Artificial control; Biological control
Copal, gum: *see* Gum copal
Coptotermes, 92
Copulation, 52
Corn, injury to, 119
Courtship, 47
Cow chips, 83, 119
Creede, Colo., 13
Creosote: *see* Coal tar creosote
Cricket, 122
Cricket-roach, 19
Crops,
  injury to by termites, 71, 103, 111, 118–119
  protection of, 161